A FIRST ELECTRONICS COURSE

A FIRST ELECTRONICS COURSE

R B Arnold BTech

Roade Comprehensive School, Northants

Stanley Thornes (Publishers) Ltd

First published in 1986 by
Stanley Thornes (Publishers) Ltd
Old Station Drive
Leckhampton
CHELTENHAM
GL53 0DN

British Library Cataloguing in Publication Data

Arnold, B.
    A first electronics course.
    1. Electronics
    I. Title
    537.5   TK7815

    ISBN 0-85950-297-X

Phototypeset by Tech-Set, Gateshead, Tyne & Wear, England
Printed at the Bath Press, Avon

CONTENTS

PREFACE

This book has been written as an introductory text for anyone who wishes to delve into the exciting world of electronics. It is suitable for use in secondary schools and middle schools, and by individual pupils who wish to take up electronics as a hobby. With this in mind I have avoided detailed mathematical and verbal descriptions and have instead included easily understood explanations of how the circuits work.

The study of electronics ought to be an active experience, so I have included a large number of experiments which require a minimum of apparatus and skill to perform. Immediately following each experiment there is a simple explanation of 'how it works'. It is not necessary to understand the explanation in order to build the circuit but an appreciation of what is happening will, I am sure, increase the sense of satisfaction and achievement experienced by pupils.

The chapters are arranged in a logical order. However, if a pupil wishes to build a circuit out of sequence, this is possible as instructions for the experiments are presented in a detailed form with the steps the pupil must take clearly numbered.

Through this book, I hope I have succeeded in opening the door to a subject which has an ever increasing relevance to everyday life.

R B Arnold
Northampton 1986

ACKNOWLEDGEMENTS

Thanks go to Mr J D Glassonbury who provided the crossword puzzles in Chapters 1, 3, 5 and 7.

Figure 5.7	Stephen James Photographic
Figure 6.11	Civil Aviation Authority
Figure 8.10	British Telecom
Figure 8.23	Barclays Bank Picture Library
Figure 8.25 (Calculator)	Trevor Yorke Commercial Photography
Figure 8.25 (TV)	Hurlstons

1 BASIC ELECTRICITY

.1 THE IMPORTANCE OF ELECTRONICS

Look around the room you are in now. If you are at home, you will probably be able to see a television set, a radio or a video recorder. If you are in a science laboratory, you may be able to see a pocket calculator, a digital watch or a power supply used in experiments. These and many other everyday objects are manufactured by electronics companies. They are examples of *electronic* devices.

Figure 1.1   *Electronic devices in everyday use.*

Meet the electron.

All *electronic* and *electrical* devices are based on the behaviour of extremely small particles called *electrons*. These particles are so small that even under a powerful microscope they cannot be seen. The 'bits and pieces' (more properly called *components*) that make up electronic devices control the movement of these electrons and make them do something useful.

Figure 1.2   *The components that make up electronic devices control the movement of electrons.*

Everyday objects such as the one shown in Figure 1.3 seem at first to be complicated, but in fact there are only seven or eight different kinds of component. In later chapters we shall take a close look at the most important components and discover how they affect the behaviour of electrons, but before we can do this we need to know a little more about electrons and electricity.

Figure 1.3   *Components inside a transistor radio.*

1.2 STATIC ELECTRICITY

Experiment 1.1

How to produce static electricity

APPARATUS: 2 × balloons; cotton thread; stand; 2 × plastic rods; a piece of cloth

PART I

1. Take two inflated balloons and rub one of them against your pullover or jumper for about 15 seconds.
2. Using a piece of cotton, suspend this balloon from a stand so that it is free to swing.
3. Now rub the second balloon against your pullover as you did in step 1 (see Figure 1.4).
4. Hold the second balloon close to but not touching the first. What happens?
5. Take off your pullover. Now hold it close to the suspended balloon. What happens?

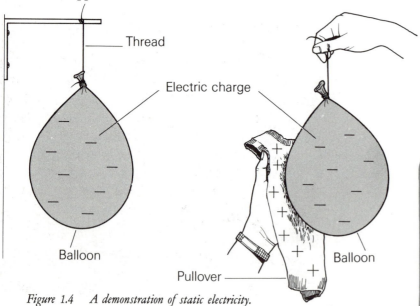

Figure 1.4   A demonstration of static electricity.

PART II

1. Take a plastic rod and a piece of cloth and rub the two together for about 15 seconds.
2. Place the rod in a paper stirrup (see Figure 1.5) and suspend it from a stand so that it is lying horizontally and is free to swing.
3. Rub a second plastic rod with the same piece of cloth.
4. Hold this second rod close to one end of the suspended rod. What happens?
5. Now hold the cloth close to one end of the suspended rod. What happens?

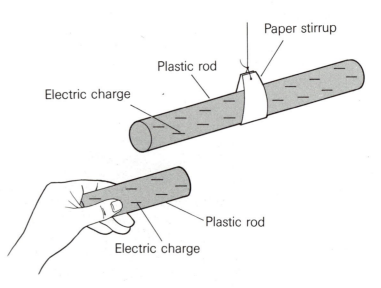

Figure 1.5   Rubbing a plastic rod with a cloth produces an electric charge.

How it works

The suspended balloon in Part I and the suspended rod in Part II both move when the other objects are held close to them. This is because all the objects have been electrically charged. In step 4 of both experiments the charged objects push away from each other, i.e. they repel, while in step 5 the charged objects attract. Because of these two different effects we believe there are two different kinds of electrical charge. We call these *positive* charges and *negative* charges.

Figure 1.6

(a)

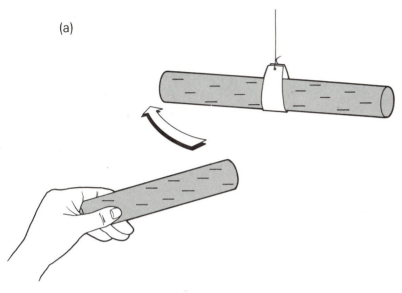

Similar charges repel.

(b)

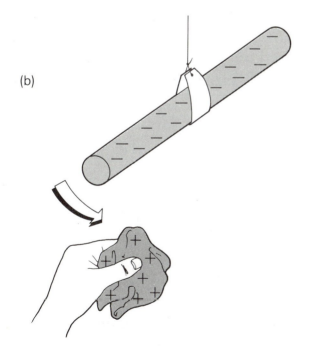

Opposite charges attract.

? This girl's hair has been charged with static electricity. Explain what is happening to it.

Figure 1.7

Where do the charges come from?

Everything around us is made from very small particles called *atoms* and we believe that inside these atoms there are even smaller particles called *protons* and *electrons*. The protons have a positive charge and the electrons a negative charge.

Normally the number of protons and electrons in an atom is equal, i.e. the atom is *neutral*, but sometimes one object may steal electrons from another simply by being rubbed against it. This results in one of the objects becoming negatively charged because it now has too many electrons, and the other object becoming positively charged because it has too few electrons (see Figure 1.8).

Objects such as these are said to be charged with *static electricity*.

(a)   (b)   Shortage of electrons

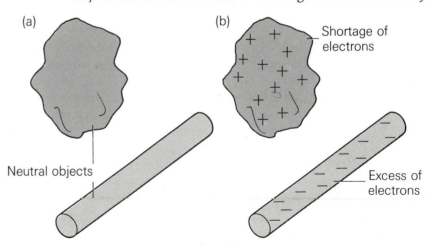

Neutral objects

Excess of electrons

Figure 1.8   Neutral and charged objects.

1.3 CELLS AND BATTERIES

Although studying static electricity is important, it is when the electrons are actually made to move that we can make most use of them. There are several ways in which we can persuade the electrons to move, but from our point of view by far the most important way is by using a *cell* or *battery*.

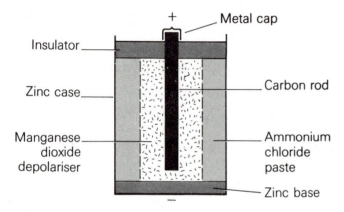

Figure 1.9   *Inside a dry cell.*

Inside a cell such as that shown in Figure 1.9 there are chemicals which react together. When they do so they produce an excess of electrons on one of the 'terminals' – this is the negative terminal – and a shortage of electrons on the other terminal – this is the positive terminal. If the two terminals are now connected by a piece of wire, electrons will flow from the negative to the positive terminal. This flow of electrons is called an *electric current* and its size is measured in *amperes* or *amps* (A). For example the headlights of a car probably have a current of about 2 amps flowing through them, while a three-bar electric fire probably needs about 12 amps.

We can think of cells and batteries as being pumps which push electrons through wires just like a water pump pushes water through pipes (see Figure 1.10).

Figure 1.10   *We can think of batteries as being electron pumps.*

If a large electric current is needed then a more powerful pump could be used. We measure the 'push' of a battery in *volts* (V). The 'push' of the batteries in Figure 1.10 is 9 volts, 4.5 volts and 3 volts.

We can also increase the 'push' of the battery by connecting together two or more cells.

When cells are connected together as in Figure 1.11 it is important to check that they are all pushing the electrons in the same direction.

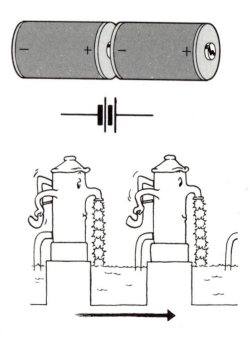

Figure 1.11   *Cells can be connected together.*

1.4 WHAT IS A CIRCUIT?

Experiment 1.2

Making and breaking a circuit

APPARATUS: Connecting wire; wire strippers; 0.06 A bulb; 9 V battery

1. Using the above apparatus build the circuit shown in Figure 1.12. N.B. The ends of the connecting wire must be 'bared'. If this has not been done, use the wire strippers to remove about ½ cm of the plastic sleeve at each end of the connecting wires.
   The bulb glows because electricity (electrons) passes through it. Throughout this book, bulbs will be used to show whether current is flowing in a circuit or not. The brightness of the bulb also gives an idea of the size of the current. How brightly do you think the bulb will glow if the current passing through it is
   a) large?
   b) small?

2. Disconnect wire A.   What happens?

3. Reconnect wire A.   Disconnect wire B.   What happens?

4. Reconnect wire B.

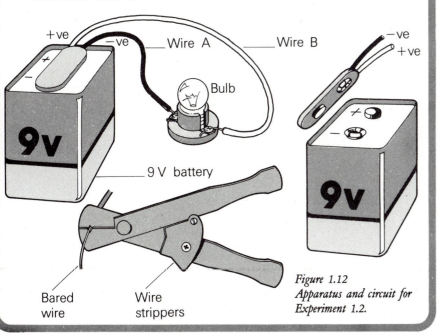

Figure 1.12
Apparatus and circuit for Experiment 1.2.

How it works

Just like water flowing through pipes, the electrons need something to travel along. If we remove one of the wires we 'break' the circuit. The electrons no longer have a complete path to follow. They stop flowing and the bulb goes out. The position of the break is unimportant. It could be before or after the bulb; the effect is still the same – electricity stops flowing. *Electricity will only flow if the circuit is complete.* We can imagine the electrons behaving as shown in Figure 1.13.

Figure 1.13   Electricity will only flow if the circuit is complete.

To draw a diagram such as Figure 1.12 each time we want to describe an electrical circuit would be difficult. To simplify things we use *circuit diagrams* (see Figure 1.14). These are simple diagrams which use symbols to represent the various components of a circuit. A complete list of symbols, diagrams and the uses of the various components can be found on page 84.

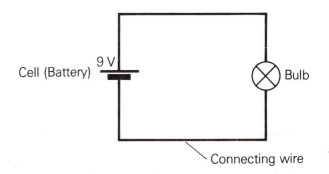

Figure 1.14 Circuit diagram for Experiment 1.2.

1.5   THE S-DeC

Although the building of the circuit for Experiment 1.2 is straight-forward and should have created few problems, more complicated circuits built this way may well suffer from faults such as poor connections. Several years ago the solution to this problem would have been to solder all the connections. This is a time-consuming solution and requires practice to be successful. To make the building of our circuits simple we will use 'S-DeCs' (see Figure 1.15). They look a little strange at first but once you have built your first circuit you will realise how easy they are to use.

Each half row of holes is connected together by strips of copper inside the S-DeC: i.e. hole numbers 1, 2, 3, 4 and 5 are all connected together; hole numbers 6, 7, 8, 9 and 10 are all connected together; hole numbers 36, 37, 38, 39 and 40 are all connected together and so on.

All connections are made by simply pushing bared wire into the appropriate hole.

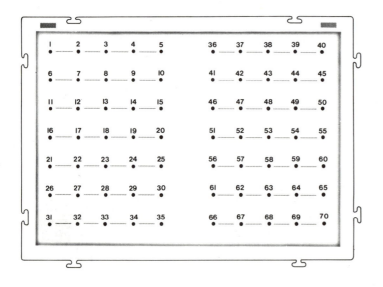

Figure 1.15   The S-DeC is used to make the building of circuits simple.

Using an S-DeC

APPARATUS: S-DeC; connecting wire; wire strippers; 0.06 A bulb; 9 V battery

Using the above apparatus try to build the circuit shown in Figure 1.16. This circuit is similar to the one you built in Experiment 1.2.

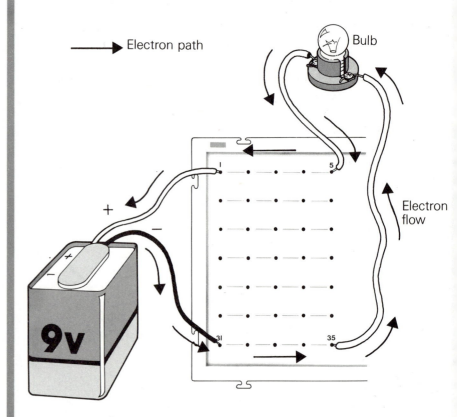

Figure 1.16   Circuit construction for Experiment 1.3.

Hint

When you push the wires into the S-DeC, do not push them too far into the holes otherwise they will kink when they touch the base of the S-DeC. It may then be difficult to pull the wires out (see Figure 1.17).

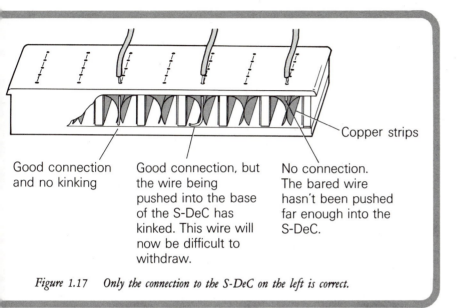

Copper strips

Good connection
and no kinking

Good connection, but
the wire being
pushed into the base
of the S-DeC has
kinked. This wire will
now be difficult to
withdraw.

No connection.
The bared wire
hasn't been pushed
far enough into the
S-DeC.

Figure 1.17   Only the connection to the S-DeC on the left is correct.

How it works

Electrons are pushed from the negative terminal of the battery down the connecting wire into hole number 31, along the copper strip inside the S-DeC, out of hole number 35 into the bulb, out of the bulb into hole number 5, along the copper strip to hole number 1 and finally back to the battery. There is a complete circuit and therefore the bulb glows. If we disconnect any of the wires – for example by pulling one of them out of a hole – the circuit becomes incomplete, no current flows and the bulb will not glow.

Conventional current

When early scientists first experimented with current electricity, they did not know which type of charge was flowing around the circuit. They guessed incorrectly that it was positive. They therefore always assumed that an electric current flowed from positive to negative.

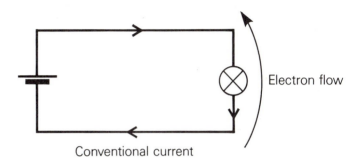

Conventional current

Even though we now know that this is incorrect it has been agreed by all scientists to continue to think of electric current as flowing from the positive to the negative. This is called *conventional current*. Nevertheless, in this book all explanations (like the previous one) will be given in terms of electron flow.

If we wanted to turn the bulb in Figure 1.16 on and off, we could do so by connecting and then disconnecting one of the wires, but it is much better to include a 'proper' switch in the circuit (see Figure 1.18).

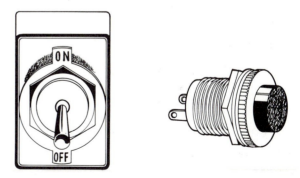

Figure 1.18   Different types of switch.

Experiment 1.4

The switch

APPARATUS: S-DeC; connecting wire; wire strippers; 0.06 A bulb; 9 V battery; switch

1. Using the above apparatus, build the circuit shown in Figure 1.19.

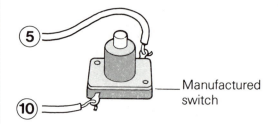

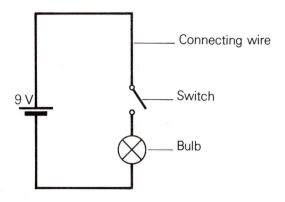

Figure 1.19   Circuit construction and diagram for Experiment 1.4.

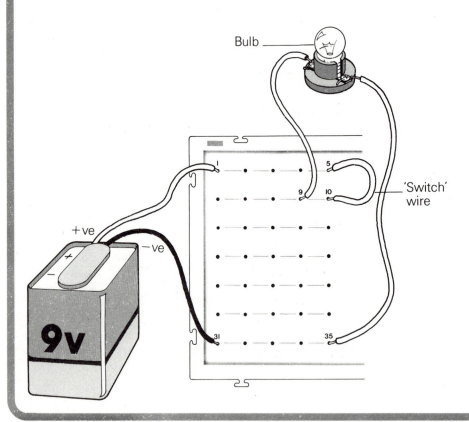

2. Open and close the switch. Explain what you see happening. We can imagine the electrons behaving as shown in Figure 1.20.

Figure 1.20   Electrons can only flow when the circuit is complete.

1.6 CONDUCTORS AND INSULATORS

Experiment 1.5

Conductors and Insulators

APPARATUS: S-DeC; connecting wire; wire strippers;
0.06 A bulb; 9 V battery

1. Using the apparatus opposite build the circuit shown in Figure 1.21.
2. Take five or six objects from your school bag or your pocket and place them one at a time across the gap.
3. Watch to see if the bulb glows or not. Read the 'How it works' below and then copy out the table and complete each column.

How it works

In step 1 the circuit is incomplete. No current can flow, and so the bulb does not glow. If a material which allows electricity to pass through it, i.e. a *conductor,* is placed across the gap, the circuit is then complete and so the bulb glows. If a material which does not allow electricity to flow through it, i.e. an *insulator,* is placed across the gap, the circuit is still incomplete and so the bulb does not glow.

Object	Insulator or conductor
Plastic comb	Insulator

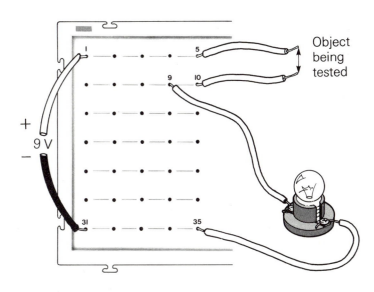

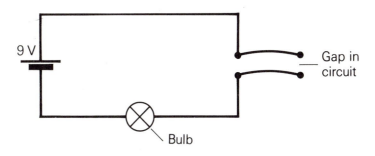

Figure 1.21   Circuit construction and diagram for Experiment 1.5.

Figure 1.22   Electrons can only flow easily through a conductor.

1.7 SERIES AND PARALLEL

There are two kinds of electrical circuit – *series* and *parallel*.

A *series* circuit is one in which the electrons have no choice as to which path to follow, i.e. there are no branches in the circuit. A *parallel* circuit is one in which the electrons do have a choice as to which path they follow.

Figure 1.23   *There are two kinds of electrical circuit.*

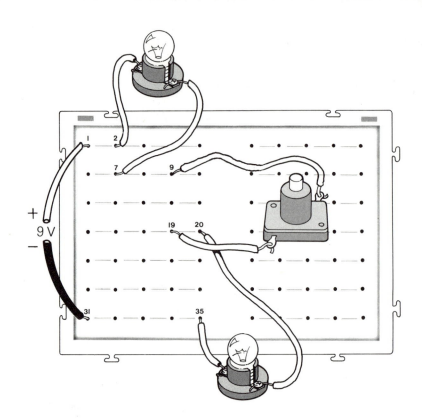

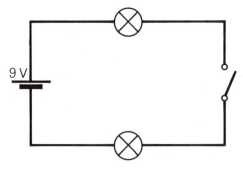

Figure 1.24   *Circuit construction and diagram for Experiment 1.6.*

Experiment 1.6

Series circuits

APPARATUS: S-DeC; wire strippers; connecting wire; 3 × 0.06 A bulbs; 9 V battery; switch

1. Using the apparatus build the circuits in Figures 1.24 and 1.25.

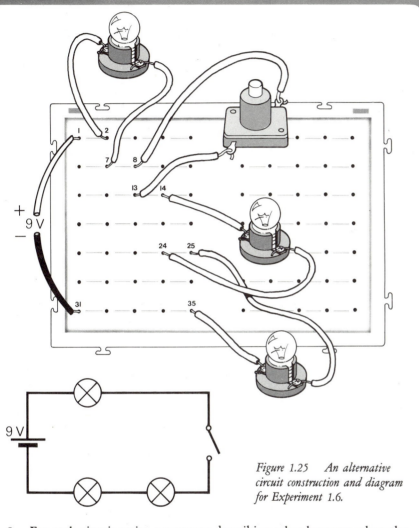

Figure 1.25   An alternative circuit construction and diagram for Experiment 1.6.

2. For each circuit write a sentence describing what happens when the switch is opened and closed.

Experiment 1.7

Parallel circuits

APPARATUS: S-DeC; connecting wire; wire strippers; 2 × 0.06 A bulbs; 9 V battery; switch

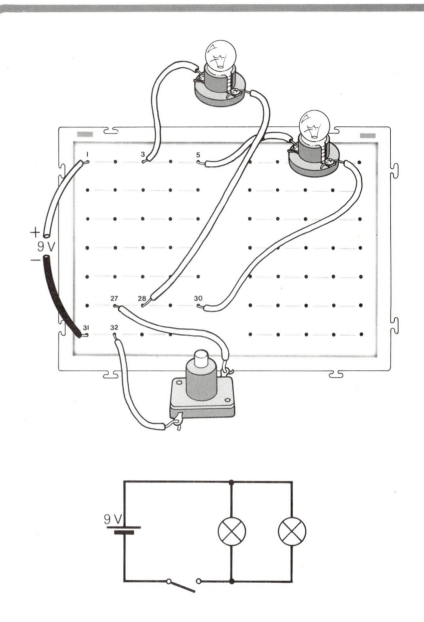

Figure 1.26   First circuit construction and diagram for Experiment 1.7.

1. Using the above apparatus build the circuits shown in Figure 1.26.
2. For each circuit write a sentence describing what happens when the switch is opened and closed.

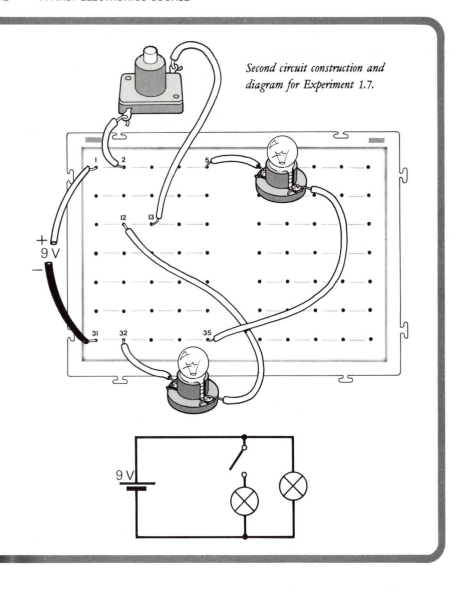

Second circuit construction and diagram for Experiment 1.7.

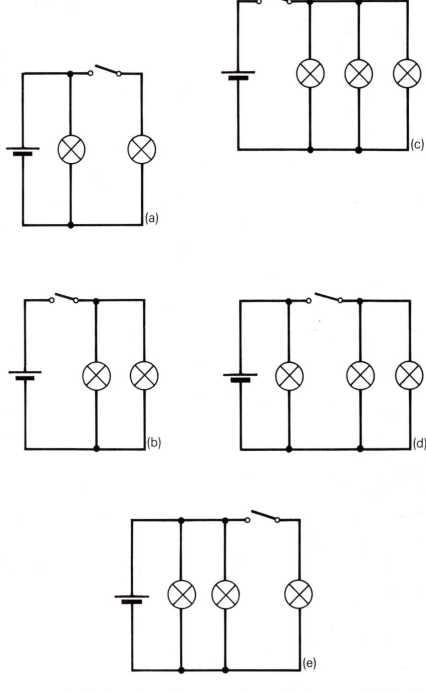

Figure 1.27   Which lamps are turned on and off by opening and closing the switches in these circuits?

How it works

From Experiments 1.6 and 1.7 you should have discovered that:

a) In a series circuit the same current passes through all the bulbs. If one of them is switched off, they are all switched off.

b) In a parallel circuit it is possible to switch off some of the bulbs and yet leave others on.

[?] Which lamps are turned on and off by opening and closing the switches in the circuits shown opposite?

1.8 RESISTORS

xperiment 1.8

What does a resistor do in a circuit?
(The dimmer switch)

APPARATUS: S-DeC; connecting wire; wire strippers;
0.06 A bulb; 9 V battery; marked resistors, 100 Ω and 200 Ω resistors;
470 Ω variable resistor   (Ω is the symbol for 'ohms')

1. Set up the circuit shown in Figure 1.28a.

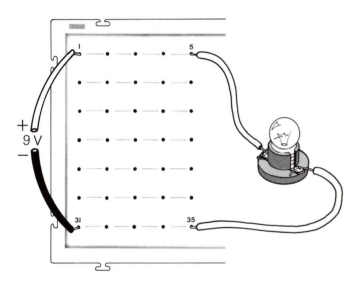

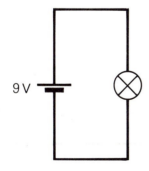

Figure 1.28(a)   Circuit construction and diagram for the first part of Experiment 1.8.

2. Look carefully at the brightness of the bulb.
3. Now alter the circuit so that the 100 Ω resistor is included as shown in Figure 1.28b.

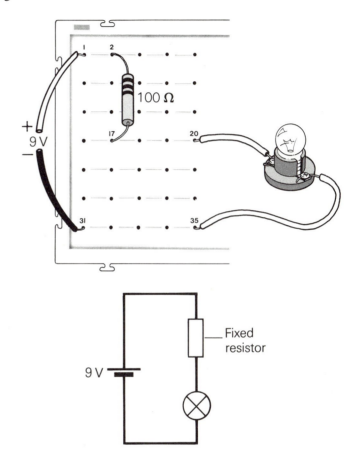

Figure 1.28(b)   Circuit construction and diagram for the second part of Experiment 1.8.

4. What do you notice about the brightness of the bulb?
5. Remove the 100 Ω resistor and replace it with a 200 Ω resistor.
6. What do you notice about the brightness of the bulb now?
7. Remove the 200 Ω resistor and replace it with a variable resistor. (See Figure 1.28c, page 14.)
8. Alter the value of the variable resistor by turning the knob.
9. What happens to the brightness of the bulb?

Figure 1.28(c)   The fixed resistor in the previous circuit has been replaced with a variable resistor.

Figure 1.30   We could imagine a resistor as being an obstacle such as a set of step ladders.

How it works

When the circuit shown in Figure 1.28a is set up the bulb shines brightly. This is because there is a 'good' flow of charge (electrons) through the bulb, but when a *resistor* is introduced into the circuit the bulb becomes dimmer indicating that the flow of charge has decreased.

If we imagine the charges (electrons) to be runners on an athletics track and the lane in which they are running as being the conductor or wire, we could imagine a resistor as being an obstacle such as a set of step ladders.

Before the resistor is introduced into the circuit the electrons flow freely around the 'track'. But when a resistor is included, a 'bottleneck' is produced which reduces the flow. The larger the value of the resistor, the _____ the bottleneck and the _____ the current that flows around the circuit.

When a *variable* resistor is included in the circuit, its value can be altered in order to increase or decrease the flow of electrons.

From the above it can be seen that the main use of resistors is to control the size of the current flowing in a circuit.

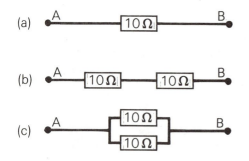

(a) A ——[10 Ω]—— B

(b) A ——[10 Ω]——[10 Ω]—— B

(c) A ——[10 Ω] / [10 Ω]—— B

Which of the circuits shown above will the electrons find

(i) most difficult
(ii) easiest

to flow through from A to B? Explain your answer.

Figure 1.29   Electrons flow easily when there is no resistance in the circuit.

.9 RESISTOR COLOUR CODING

As you can see in Figure 1.31 resistors are often quite small. So small in fact that it would be difficult to write their values on them. To overcome this problem resistors are usually marked with four coloured bands. From the first three bands the value of a resistor can be worked out. The fourth band tells us how accurate the value of the resistor is. (This is known as the *tolerance* and will not be discussed in this book.)

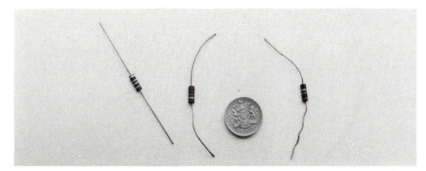

Figure 1.31   Resistors are often quite small.

OW TO READ THE COLOUR CODING

Hold the resistor so that the coloured bands are to the left. Then using the table below work out the value of your resistor:

1st Band 1st Digit		2nd Band 2nd Digit		3rd Band Number of Zeros	
Black	0	Black	0	Black	No zeros
Brown	1	Brown	1	Brown	One zero
Red	2	Red	2	Red	Two zeros
Orange	3	Orange	3	Orange	Three zeros
Yellow	4	Yellow	4	Yellow	Four zeros
Green	5	Green	5	Green	Five zeros
Blue	6	Blue	6	Blue	Six zeros
Violet	7	Violet	7	Violet	Seven zeros
Grey	8	Grey	8	Grey	Eight zeros
White	9	White	9	White	Nine zeros

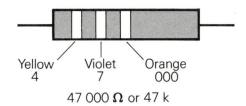

Yellow 4   Violet 7   Orange 000
47 000 Ω or 47 k

If the first band is yellow, the table shows that this means the first number in the resistance value is 4.

If the second band is violet this means that the second number in the resistance value is 7.

If the third band is orange this means that three zeros follow the first two numbers.

The value of this resistor is therefore 47 000 Ω, more usually written as 47 k (short for 47 kΩ, k for kilo). A resistor whose value is 47 000 000 Ω would be written as 47 M (short for 47 MΩ, M for mega).

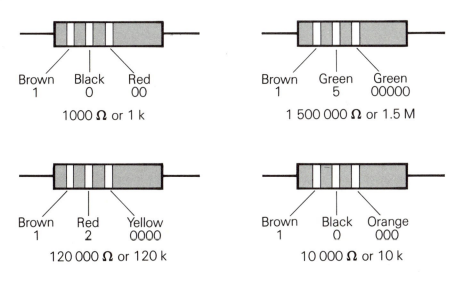

Figure 1.32   Examples of colour coded resistor values.

Using the table on page 15, check the values of the resistors shown in Figure 1.33.

When a decimal point occurs in the resistor value, a way of writing this is to replace the decimal point with a k or an M, depending on whether the resistor's value is being given in kilo or mega ohms.

For example, 4.7 k can be written as 4k7. This is the method used in this book.

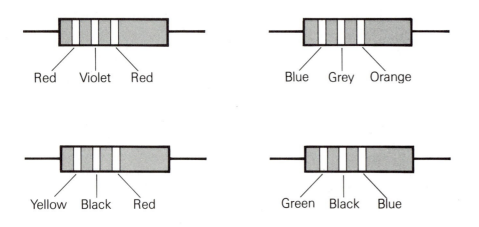

Red   Violet   Red

Blue   Grey   Orange

Yellow   Black   Red

Green   Black   Blue

Figure 1.33   What are the values of these resistors?

1.10 THERMISTORS AND LIGHT DEPENDENT RESISTORS (LDRs)

Experiment 1.9

What is a thermistor and what does it do?

APPARATUS: S-DeC; connecting wire; wire strippers; 0.06 A bulb; 9 V battery; thermistor (TH3); matches

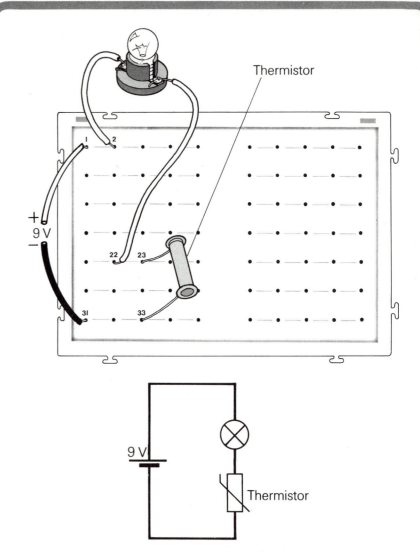

Figure 1.34   Circuit construction and diagram for Experiment 1.9.

1. Set up the circuit as shown in Figure 1.34.
2. Look carefully at the brightness of the bulb.
3. Gently warm the thermistor with a match.
4. What do you notice about the brightness of the bulb?

Can you suggest what must be happening to alter the brightness of the bulb?

How it works

A *thermistor* is a special kind of resistor whose value changes as its temperature alters. In Experiment 1.9, when the thermistor is heated its resistance decreases. As a result the bulb shines more brightly. This property of a thermistor, to change resistance as its temperature changes, has many important practical applications such as in fire alarms and thermostats.

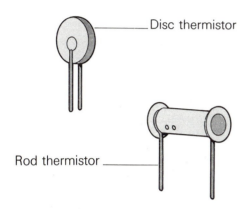

Figure 1.35   Two types of thermistor.

Experiment 1.10

What is a light dependent resistor (LDR) and what does it do?

APPARATUS: S-DeC; connecting wire; wire strippers; 0.06 A bulb; 9 V battery; torch or any source of bright light; LDR (ORP 12)

1. Set up the circuit as shown in Figure 1.36.

2. Look carefully at the bulb.

3. Shine a strong light onto the LDR.

4. What happens to the brightness of the bulb?
   Can you suggest what must be happening to alter the brightness of the bulb?

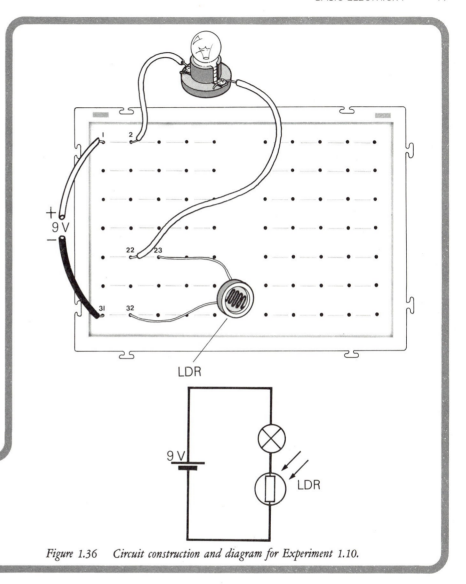

Figure 1.36   Circuit construction and diagram for Experiment 1.10.

How it works

An LDR is a special kind of resistor whose value alters when light shines on it. In Experiment 1.10 when sufficient light falls on the LDR its resistance decreases. As a result the bulb shines more brightly. This property of an LDR to change resistance as the intensity (brightness) of light changes has many important practical applications such as in burglar alarms, automatic light control, etc. (See Chapter 4.)

Light

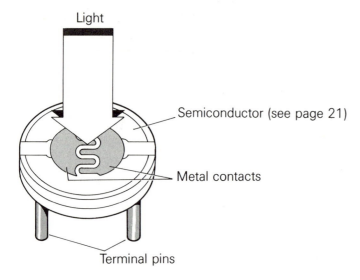

Semiconductor (see page 21)

Metal contacts

Terminal pins

Figure 1.37   Construction of a light dependent resistor (LDR).

QUESTION TIME, FOLKS!

QUESTIONS ON CHAPTER 1

Write down the correct words to fill the gaps in these sentence
Do *not* write on this page.

1. Similar charges _____ but opposite charges _____

2. The flow of charge is called a _____ and we measur
    it in _____ .

3. All electronics is based on the behaviour of small particle
    called _____ .

4. There are two main types of circuit; these are _____
    circuits and _____ circuits.

5. We can control the current flowing in a circuit by using
    _____ .

6. Using the colour code, work out the values of the resistor
    shown below.

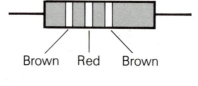

Brown   Red   Brown

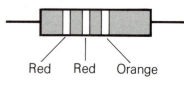

Red   Red   Orange

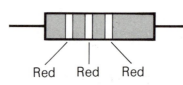

Red   Red   Red

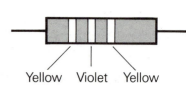

Yellow   Violet   Yellow

7. What is the colour code for a resistor whose value is
    a) 470 Ω
    b) 33 000 Ω
    c) 10 Ω
    d) 1 M
    e) 1 k

8. What is a thermistor?

9. What is a light dependent resistor?

10. Suggest one use for a thermistor and one use for a ligh
    dependent resistor.

CROSSWORD ON CHAPTER 1

Across

1 If you _____ the switch in a circuit, current will flow. (5)

4 This kind of material will allow current to pass through it. (9)

5 A switch could simply be a piece of _____ . (4)

6 A _____ glows more brightly as more current flows through it. (4)

8 The value of a resistor is shown by coloured rings; each one is called a _____ . (4)

10 Unlike charges _____ . (7)

12 Current flow is measured in _____ . (4)

14 A complete path for electrons to flow around is called a _____ . (7)

16 If the current flowing through a 6 across is reduced it becomes _____ . (3)

18 Unit of electrical resistance. (3)

19 The amount of _____ from a 6 across depends upon how much current is flowing through it. (5)

20 A 6 across will _____ when current flows through it. (4)

21 Any _____ device uses electricity. (10)

Down

2 If you _____ the switch in a circuit, no current can flow. (4)

3 A tiny particle with a negative charge. (8)

4 An object with too many, or too few electrons, is said to be _____ . (7)

7 If we create a _____ in a circuit, current will cease to flow. (5)

8 More than one 14 down connected together form a _____ . (7)

9 Items such as calculators and digital watches are known as _____ devices. (10)

10 An important application of a thermistor is its use as a fire _____ . (5)

11 An _____ will not allow current to pass through it. (9)

13 A special kind of resistor whose value changes when light shines on it. (3)

14 This pushes charges around a circuit. (4)

15 A 14 down can be considered to be a kind of _____ . (4)

17 An electric current is a _____ of charge. (4)

2 DIODES AND CAPACITORS

2.1 THE DIODE

1. Set up the circuit as shown in Figure 2.1a.
2. Look carefully at the brightness of the bulb.
3. Alter the circuit so that the diode is now included, as shown in Figure 2.1b. Make sure that: a) the band marked on the diode is nearest to hole number 23 b) the positive terminal of the battery is connected to hole number 1 and the negative terminal to hole number 31.
4. What do you notice about the brightness of the bulb?
5. Now reverse the diode connections so that the band is nearest to hole number 3.
6. What do you notice about the brightness of the bulb?

Experiment 2.1

What does a diode do in a circuit?

APPARATUS: S-DeC; connecting wire; wire strippers; 0.06 A bulb; 9 V battery; diode (1N4001)

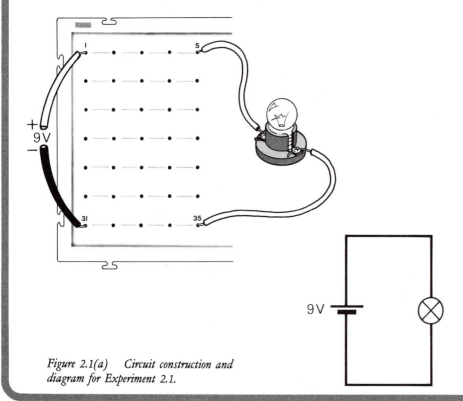

Diode

Band

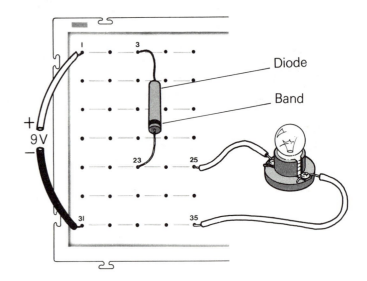

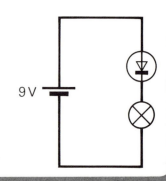

Figure 2.1(a)   Circuit construction and diagram for Experiment 2.1.

Figure 2.1(b)   A diode is now included in the circuit for Experiment 2.1.

ow it works

When the circuit shown in Figure 2.1a is set up, the bulb shines brightly showing that the electrons are flowing freely around the circuit. The introduction of the *diode* as in Figure 2.1b causes the bulb to dim as if the diode is a type of resistor. But when the position of the diode is reversed, the bulb does not shine at all, i.e. little or no current is flowing around the circuit.

A diode is in fact a kind of 'one way street'. Electrons can move through it in one direction but not in the opposite direction. We can imagine the diode to be behaving like the step ladders in Figure 2.2.

Conducting diode

Non conducting diode

Figure 2.2 Electrons can move through a diode in one direction, but not in the other direction.

2.2 THE STRUCTURE OF A DIODE

In Experiment 1.5 we tested various materials to see if they were conductors or insulators. The conductors allowed charges to flow through them but the insulators did not. There is a third group of materials which lies midway between these two extremes. These materials are called *semiconductors*. A good example of a semiconducting material is pure silicon. At room temperature pure silicon does allow charge to flow through it but not very easily. However, if certain impurities are added (a process called *doping*), its conductivity can be improved. We can do this in two ways:

1. The conductivity can be improved by adding an impurity such as phosphorus or arsenic. This produces *n-type* silicon.

2. The conductivity can be improved by adding an impurity such as indium or gallium. This produces *p-type* silicon.

Both n-type and p-type silicon have better conductivities than pure silicon at room temperature (see Figure 2.3).

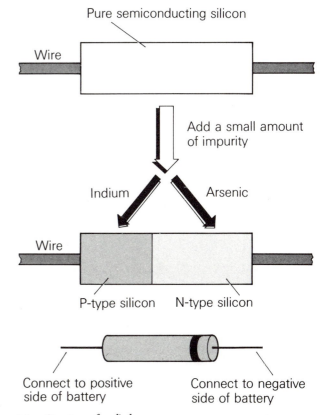

Figure 2.3 Structure of a diode.

The diode used in Experiment 2.1 consists of a piece of p-type silicon in contact with a piece of n-type silicon.

If the positive terminal of the battery is connected to the p-type silicon and the negative terminal to the n-type silicon, current will flow easily through the diode. But if the connections are reversed, current is unable to flow through the diode. The n-type silicon end of a diode is usually marked by a band.

2.3 LIGHT EMITTING DIODES (LEDs)

Experiment 2.2

What does an LED do in a circuit?

APPARATUS: S-DeC; connecting wire; wire strippers; 0.06 A bulb 9 V battery; LED; 510 Ω resistor (green brown brown)

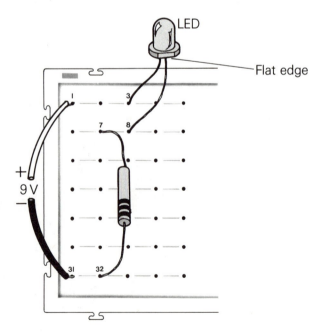

Figure 2.4(a)   Circuit construction for Experiment 2.2.

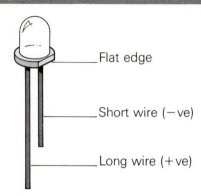

Figure 2.4(b)   Identifying the connections to a light emitting diode.

1. Set up the circuit as shown in Figure 2.4(a). Make sure that the LED is connected in the circuit so that the flat edge of its body is above the leg which is connected to hole number 8.

2. What do you notice about the LED?

3. Now reverse the position of the LED so that the flat edge is above the leg which is connected to hole number 3.

4. What do you notice about the LED?

5. Remove the LED and replace it with a bulb.

6. Look carefully at the bulb. Is it glowing?

How it works

 If the LED is connected as shown in Figure 2.5a it glows, showin that it is conducting electricity, but if the connections of the LED a reversed (see Figure 2.5b) it does not glow. This is because, like oth

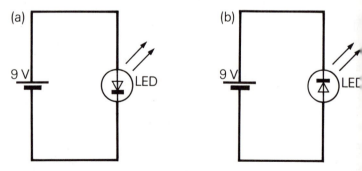

Figure 2.5   In (a) the light emitting diode will glow. Connected as in (b) it will not glow.

diodes, it only conducts in one direction. When the bulb replaces the LED it does not glow. It is not a diode and therefore it must conduct electricity regardless of which way it is connected. The current flowing around the circuit must therefore be too small to make the bulb glow.

From this we can see that LEDs need less current to make them glow than do bulbs, but they are not as bright. LEDs therefore are used in situations where the brightness of the light is not important. Their main use is to show that electricity is flowing in the circuit, i.e. to show that a piece of electrical equipment is turned on and working.

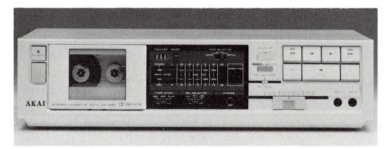

Figure 2.6   Electronic device using LED displays.

4 THE CAPACITOR

A *capacitor* is a device which is used to store electrical charge. It usually consists of two metal plates placed close together with an insulator between them. The insulator may be air, but is often a thin sheet of plastic.

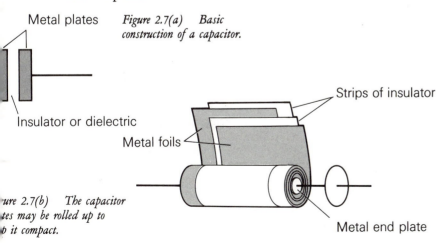

Metal plates

Figure 2.7(a)   Basic construction of a capacitor.

Insulator or dielectric

Metal foils

Strips of insulator

Metal end plate

ure 2.7(b)   The capacitor tes may be rolled up to o it compact.

If we want to store a large amount of charge, a capacitor with large metal plates is needed. In order to keep these compact, the plates are often 'rolled up' as shown in Figure 2.7b. We usually measure the value of a capacitor in µF or pF.

µF stands for *microfarad* which equals one millionth of a farad.

pF stands for *picofarad* which equals one million millionths of a farad.

The larger the value, the more charge the capacitor can store.

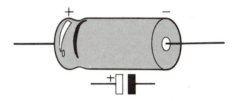

Figure 2.7(c)   An electrolytic capacitor.

Figure 2.7c illustrates a special kind of capacitor called an *electrolytic capacitor.* When you use this kind of capacitor you *must* connect it into the circuit the right way round (see Figure 2.7c) otherwise you will damage it.

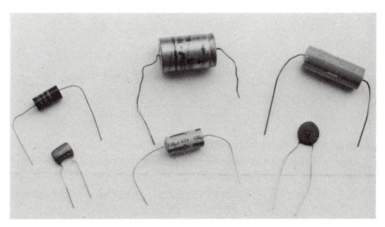

Figure 2.7(d)   Different types of capacitor.

Experiment 2.3

Charging and discharging a capacitor

APPARATUS: S-DeC; connecting wire; wire strippers; 9 V battery; LED; 2200 µF electrolytic capacitor

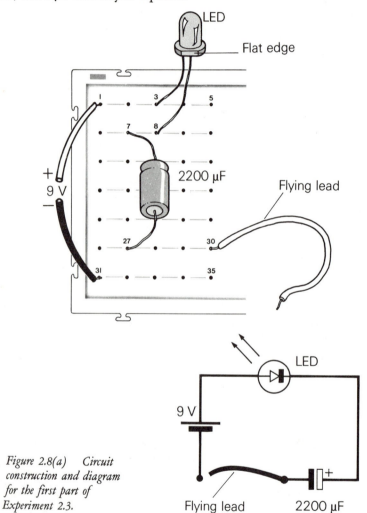

Figure 2.8(a)   Circuit construction and diagram for the first part of Experiment 2.3.

1. Set up the circuit shown in Figure 2.8a. Make sure that:
   a) the battery connections are correct (+ve to hole number 1, −ve to hole number 31).
   b) the electrolytic capacitor and LED are also connected the right way round.

2. Connect the loose end of the flying lead to hole number 35. What happens to the LED?

3. Disconnect the flying lead from hole number 35.

4. Reverse the connections to the LED as shown in Figure 2.8b.

5. Connect the loose end of the flying lead to hole number 5.

6. What happens to the LED?

7. Now repeat stages 1 to 6. In your exercise book write two or three sentences describing precisely what you see happen.

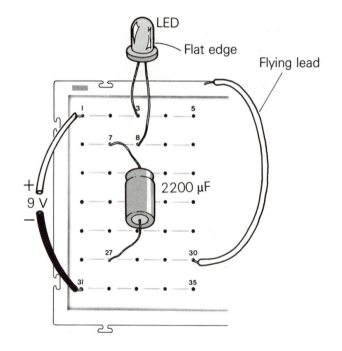

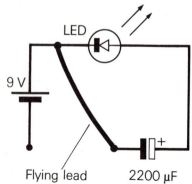

Figure 2.8(b)   Circuit construction and diagram for the second part of Experiment 2.3.

ow it works

When the circuit shown in Figure 2.8a is set up, and the flying lead is connected between holes 30 and 35, electrons from the negative terminal of the battery set out on their 'jog' around the circuit, but soon the electrons realise that it is a false start and they cannot complete the whole circuit because there is a gap between the two plates of the capacitor. The electrons on the plate realise this but the electrons behind them do not. So more and more electrons are pushed on to the plate. Eventually the plate becomes 'overcrowded', the 'traffic jam' is complete and the electrons stop flowing.

Figure 2.9   Charging a capacitor.

While all this has been happening on the negative plate of the capacitor, electrons on the positive plate have also been moving. This movement is due to:

1. The repulsive forces from the electrons gathering on the negative plate.

2. The attractive forces which come from the positive terminal of the battery.

Summing up the situation described above we can say that when the flying lead is connected between holes 30 and 35, current begins to flow. This flow 'charges up' the capacitor. As the capacitor becomes fully charged the current decreases and eventually stops.

Now look back at the notes you wrote about Experiment 2.3.

? Does the behaviour of the LED agree with the explanation just given? Explain why it does or does not.

When the circuit is altered to look like that shown in Figure 2.8b, the capacitor is still 'charged', i.e. it has a surplus of electrons on one plate and a shortage of electrons on the other plate. We know that opposite charges attract, so when the flying lead is connected to hole number 5 the electrons flow from the negative plate through the LED to the positive plate. This flow 'discharges' the capacitor and when there is no longer an imbalance of charge the flow stops.

Figure 2.10   Discharging a capacitor.

Again look back at the notes you wrote about Experiment 2.3.

? Does the behaviour of the LED agree with the above explanation? Explain. Why was it necessary to change the connections of the diode each time the capacitor was charged or discharged?

Experiment 2.4

Charging and discharging a capacitor through a resistor

APPARATUS: S-DeC; connecting wire; wire strippers; 9 V battery; LED; resistors, 10 Ω (brown black black), 100 Ω (brown black brown), 330 Ω (orange orange brown); electrolytic capacitors 2200 μF, 100 μF, 10 μF

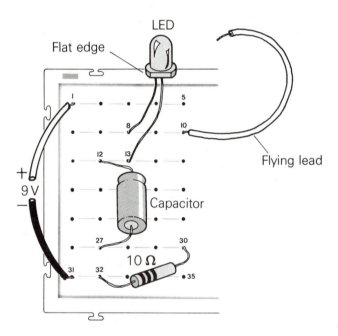

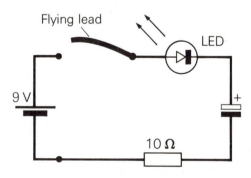

Figure 2.11(a)   Circuit construction and diagram for Experiment 2.4.

1. Set up the circuit shown in Figure 2.11a. Make sure that:
    a) the battery connections are correct (+ve to hole number 1, −ve to hole number 31)
    b) the electrolytic capacitor and the LED are also connected the right way round.
2. Connect the loose end of the flying lead to hole number 5. Look carefully at the LED. Does it glow for a short, medium or long time?
3. Disconnect the flying lead from hole number 5.
4. Reverse the connections of the LED as shown in Figure 2.11b.
5. Connect the loose end of the flying lead to hole number 35. Again observe the behaviour of the LED.
6. Replace the 10 Ω resistor with the 100 Ω resistor. Then repeat steps 1 to 5.
7. Replace the 100 Ω resistor with a 330 Ω resistor. Then repeat steps 1 to 5.
8. Now repeat steps 1 to 6, but using a 100 μF capacitor and then a 10 μF capacitor in place of the 2200 μF capacitor.

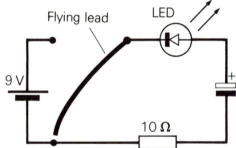

Figure 2.11(b)
Discharging the capacitor.

Write several sentences explaining what you have discovered from this experiment. Pay particular attention to the brightness and length of the flash of the LED. Explain how these alter when the value of the resistor or capacitor is changed.

Study your results carefully and see if they agree with these conclusions:

1. If the size of the capacitor is increased, more charge can be stored in it. Therefore the charging and discharging times increase.
2. If we charge or discharge a capacitor through a resistor, it impedes the flow of electrons and therefore increases the charging and discharging times.

UESTIONS ON CHAPTER 2

Write down the correct words to fill the gaps in these sentences.

1. The main purpose of a capacitor is to store _____ .

2. Most capacitors consist of two metal plates with an _____ sandwiched between them.

3. A diode allows current to flow in one _____ only.

4. When current flows through an LED it _____ .

5. Explain what is meant by:
   a) a semiconducting material.
   b) an n-type semiconductor.
   c) a p-type semiconductor.

6. Draw a labelled diagram of the structure of a capacitor.

7. Draw a labelled diagram of the structure of a diode. Which way must the diode be connected if it is to conduct?

The circuit below contains four components and a switch. By solving each of the clues following the diagram and then inserting the first letter of each answer, you should be able to work out what the components are.

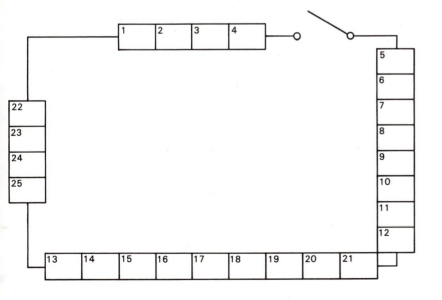

(1) These allow electricity to flow through them.

(2) It's what this book is all about.

(3) We usually use a bulb if we want this.

(4) Capacitors have two; dogs have four.

(5) When a circuit is complete the electrons can travel all the way _____ it.

(6) Gives off.

(7) You already know that this component is included in this circuit.

(8) To improve the conductivity of 9 add an _____ .

(9) A semiconductor.

(10) The value of a red band on a resistor.

(11) Don't turn it on, leave it _____ .

(12) A conducting diode will not conduct if its connections are _____ .

(13) This 'pumps' electrons around a circuit.

(14) We measure the size of a 17 in _____ .

(15) Capacitors have two of these.

(16) Opposite charges do this.

(17) A flow of charge.

(18) These don't allow charges to flow through them.

(19) A special resistor which is sensitive to temperature change.

(20) We measure resistance in _____ .

(21) What is the colour of a 2k2 resistor?

(22) Several 13s connected together.

(23) To control the size of a 17 we _____ resistors.

(24) A diode which glows when current is passing through it.

(25) Coloured _____ indicate the value of a resistor.

What happens when the switch in this circuit is closed?

3 THE TRANSISTOR

3.1 STRUCTURE OF A TRANSISTOR

There are several different types of transistor. The one we shall use is called a *junction transistor.* It, like the diode mentioned in Chapter 2, is made from semiconducting materials, usually silicon or germanium. As Figure 3.1 shows, the transistor has three terminals or 'legs'. This is because the semiconducting materials are arranged like a thin sandwich. The sandwich can either be npn or pnp. The transistors that you will use (transistor 2N3053) are all of the npn type.

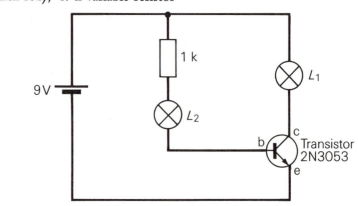

Figure 3.2   Identification of the transistor terminals is by means of a tag. On the right is a view from below.

The three terminals of a transistor are the *base,* the *collector* and the *emitter.*

When you connect a transistor into a circuit you must make sure that these three terminals are connected correctly, otherwise the transistor will be damaged. Although the connections are not labelled they can be identified from the shape of the transistor (see Figure 3.2).

Let us now have a look at what a transistor does in a circuit.

3.2 THE TRANSISTOR SWITCH
Experiment 3.1

The transistor switch

APPARATUS: S-DeC; connecting wire; wire strippers; 2 × 0.06 A bulbs; 9 V battery; transistor 2N3053; 1 k resistor (brown black red); 47 k variable resistor

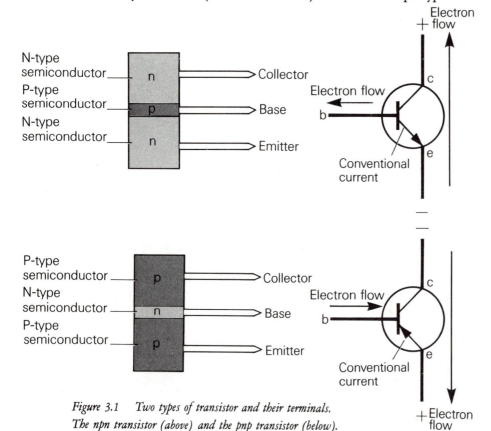

Figure 3.1   Two types of transistor and their terminals. The npn transistor (above) and the pnp transistor (below).

Figure 3.3   Circuit diagram and construction for Experiment 3.1.

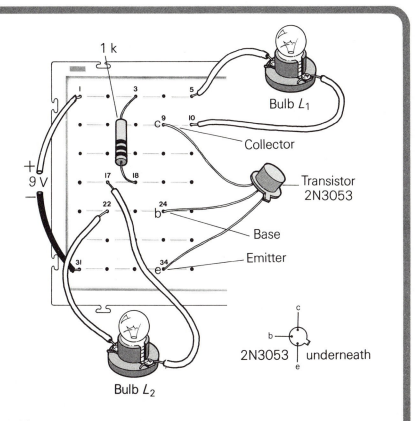

 ## PART I

1. Set up the circuit as shown in Figure 3.3. Be careful to connect the three terminals of the transistor and the connecting wires from the battery to the correct holes.
   Does the bulb L_1 glow? Does the bulb L_2 glow?
2. Unscrew bulb L_2. What happens to bulb L_1?

How It works

When the circuit is initially set up, bulb L_1 glows quite brightly showing that there is a good flow of current through the transistor and the bulb L_1.

But bulb L_2 does not glow. There are two possible reasons for this:

1. There is no electricity flowing in this part of the circuit.
2. There is current flowing in this part of the circuit, but it is too small to make the bulb glow.

If there is no current flowing through bulb L_2, unscrewing it and taking it out of its holder ought not to affect the circuit, but this is not the case. When bulb L_2 is unscrewed bulb L_1 goes out.

We can conclude from this that when a small current flows in the base circuit of a transistor a much larger current can flow between the collector and the emitter. But when there is no current flowing in the base circuit there can be no current flowing between the collector and the emitter. We can summarise this situation by saying that the base current is switching the collector-emitter current on and off.

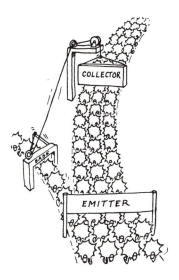

Figure 3.4 A small current flowing in the base circuit of a transistor can control a large current flowing in the collector-emitter circuit.

PART II

1. Still using the circuit shown in Figure 3.3 remove the bulb L_2 and its holder and insert in its place the 47 k variable resistor.
2. Very slowly alter the value of the variable resistor. What happens to the brightness of bulb L_1?

How it works

 When the value of the variable resistor is altered, this affects the size of the current flowing in the base circuit of the transistor, which in turn affects the size of the much larger current in the collector-emitter circuit. This means that the transistor is amplifying the changes in the base current.

From this we can see that transistors can be used:

1. as 'electronic switches'
2. as 'amplifiers'.

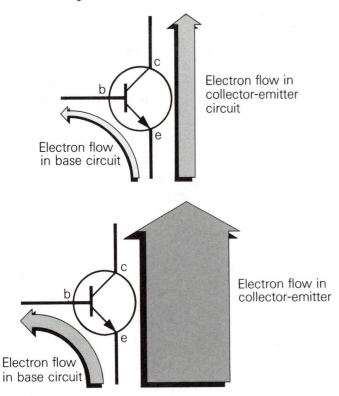

Figure 3.5   The base current controls the size of the collector-emitter current.

Experiment 3.2

Switching by light
(The Automatic Parking Light)

APPARATUS: S-DeC; connecting wire; wire strippers; 0.06 A bulb; 9 V battery; transistor 2N3053; LDR (ORP12); 10 k resistor (brown black orange)

1. Set up the circuit shown in Figure 3.6.
2. Cover the LDR with a thick piece of cloth or perhaps a handkerchief. What happens to bulb L_1?

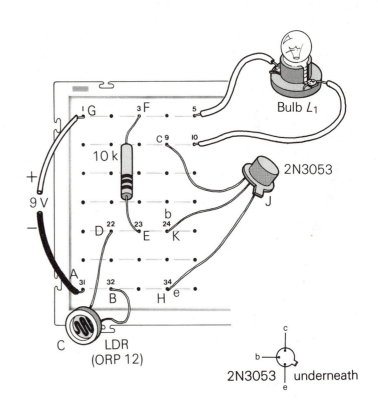

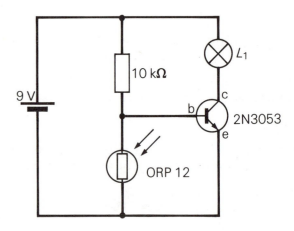

Figure 3.6   Circuit construction and diagram for Experiment 3.2.

How it works

When the circuit is first set up, light is reaching the LDR and so its resistance is low (see page 17). Because of this most electrons leaving the negative terminal of the cell find it easier to follow the path A B C D E F G. There is therefore almost no current flowing in the base circuit of the transistor. Consequently, the collector–emitter circuit is switched off and bulb L_1 does not glow. When the LDR is covered up, no light reaches it and therefore its resistance is high. The current now finds it easier to follow the path A H J K E F G. Because there is now current in the base circuit, the collector-emitter circuit is switched on and bulb L_1 glows.

This kind of circuit could be used as an automatic parking light. During the day the daylight switches the transistor off, but at night the lack of light switches the transistor on and the bulb glows.

3. Swap the positions of the 10 k resistor and the LDR.

4. Cover the LDR with your cloth. What happens?

5. Uncover the LDR. What happens? What might this circuit be used for?

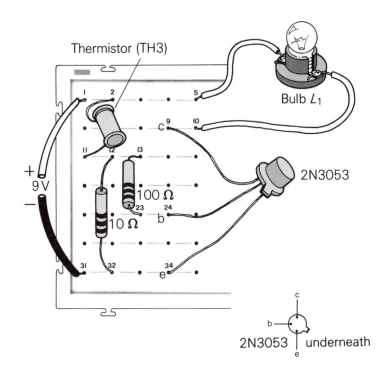

Experiment 3.3

Switching by temperature (The Fire Alarm)

APPARATUS: S-DeC; connecting wire; wire strippers; 0.06 A bulb; 9 V battery; transistor 2N3053; resistors, 10 Ω (brown black black), 100 Ω (brown black brown), 1 k (brown black red); thermistor (TH3)

1. Set up the circuit as shown in Figure 3.7.

2. Heat the thermistor using a match. What happens to bulb L_1? Read carefully the explanation of how the 'automatic parking light' circuit works in Experiment 3.2.
    Now try to explain how this circuit works and how it could be used as a fire alarm.

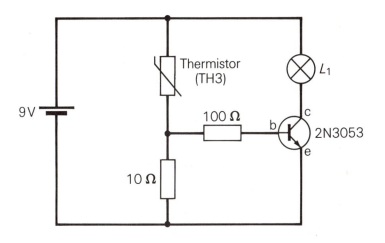

Figure 3.7   Circuit construction and diagram for Experiment 3.3.

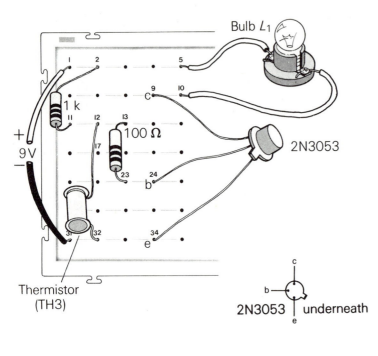

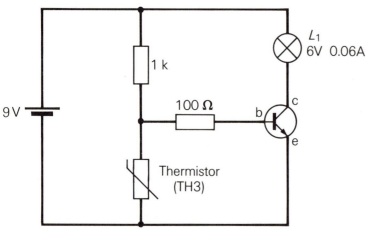

Figure 3.8   The modified circuit for Experiment 3.3.

3. Alter the circuit as shown in Figure 3.8.

4. Heat the thermistor using a match. What happens to the bulb L_1? What could this circuit be used for?

Experiment 3.4

What is the effect of putting a capacitor in the base circuit?

APPARATUS: S-DeC; connecting wire; wire strippers; 0.06 A bulb; 9 V battery; transistor 2N3053; resistor 4k7 (yellow violet red); capacitors, 100 µF, 220 µF, 470 µF, 1000 µF, 2200 µF; stopwatch

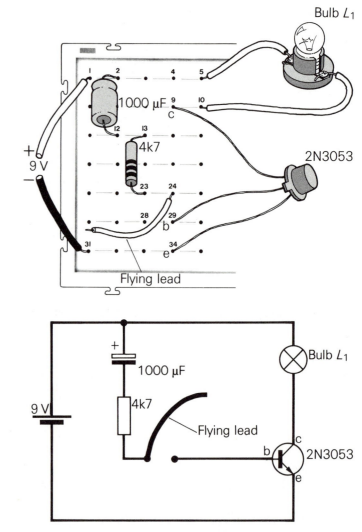

Figure 3.9   Circuit construction and diagram for Experiment 3.4.

1. Set up the circuit as shown in Figure 3.9. Before connecting the battery check that the transistor and the capacitor are connected the right way round.

2. Connect the flying lead from hole number 24 to hole number 28. What happens to bulb L_1?

3. Discharge the capacitor by connecting the flying lead from hole number 24 to hole number 4.

4. When the capacitor is fully discharged (after about 30 seconds), repeat step 2 but this time, using your stopwatch, measure the time for which the bulb glows.

5. Repeat step 4 with a 220 μF, 470 μF, 1000 μF and finally a 2200 μF capacitor.

6. Draw a table similar to that shown below and fill in your results.

Capacitor	Resistor	Time

Turn back to Chapter 2, Experiment 2.4 and remind yourself of the effect of having a capacitor and a resistor in a circuit. Now explain in detail what happens when the capacitor is being charged up and what effect this has on the collector–emitter current.

QUESTIONS ON CHAPTER 3

Write down the correct words to fill the gaps in these sentences.

1. A junction transistor has three terminals or legs. These are the _____ , the _____ and the _____ .

2. If no current flows into the _____ , the transistor is switched _____ .

3. If current flows into the _____ , the transistor is switched _____ .

4. Draw a labelled diagram of an npn transistor.

5. Draw a diagram of a 2N3053 npn transistor and explain how each of the terminals can be identified.

6. What are the two main uses of a transistor?

CROSSWORD ON CHAPTER 3

Across

1   What this chapter is all about. The _____ . (10)

3   The three terminals of a transistor are often called the _____ . (4)

5   A circuit whose output is greater than its input is called an _____ . (9)

8   A thermistor detects changes of temperature and can be used to give warning of _____ . (4)

9   Flexible connecting material. (4)

11 A transistor has two main uses. One is a 5 across. The second is a _____ . (6)

13 An important application of an LDR is its use as a _____ alarm. (7)

15 A short circuit connected across a 12 down will _____ it. (9)

16 A device used to control the size of a current flowing in a circuit. (8)

17 This measurement indicates how strongly a cell or battery pushes charges around the circuit. (4)

19 The positive terminal of an npn transistor. (9)

Down

1   A transistor has three _____ . (9)

2   When no current flows in the base circuit of a transistor, the transistor is switched _____ . (3)

4   A good example of a semiconductor is _____ . (7)

6   An LDR can be used to construct a _____ light. (7)

7   The negative 1 down of an npn transistor. (7)

10 A 12 down can be used to store this. (6)

12 An electrolytic _____ must be connected the correct way around. (9)

13 The 1 down of a transistor between the emitter and the collector. (4)

14 Charging a 12 down through a resistor can be used as an accurate _____ . (5)

18 When current flows in the base circuit of a transistor, the transistor is switched _____ . (2)

4 SWITCHING USING TRANSISTORS

4.1 THE TWO-TRANSISTOR SWITCH

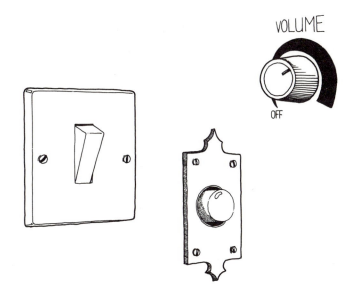

Figure 4.1   Three different types of switch.

In Figure 4.1 we can see just a few of the many different types of switch that can be found in the home. Some are turned, some are pressed, and with some a small lever is moved up and down. Switches like these are often too big or too slow to be of any use in electronic equipment. As we have seen in Chapter 3, a transistor can be used as a simple switch; but if two transistors are connected together several different types of switch can be constructed.

Before we do this we need to investigate what happens in a simple two-transistor circuit.

To build and investigate a simple two-transistor circuit

APPARATUS: S-DeC; connecting wire; wire strippers; 2 × 0.06 A bulbs; 9 V battery; 2 × transistors 2N3053; 2 × 1 k resistors (brown black red)

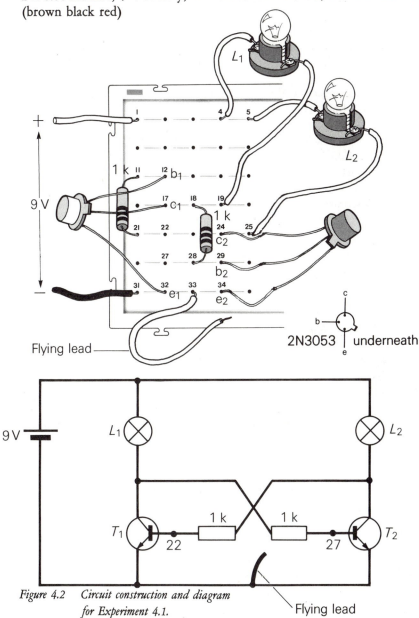

Figure 4.2   Circuit construction and diagram for Experiment 4.1.

1. Set up the circuit as shown in Figure 4.2. Notice that the two bulbs L_1 and L_2 are connected to the collector terminals of transistors T_1 and T_2 respectively. If L_1 glows this shows that T_1 is switched on. If L_2 glows this shows that T_2 is switched on.

2. Connect the flying lead from hole number 33 to hole number 22. Look carefully at each bulb then answer these questions. Is T_1 switched on or off? Is T_2 switched on or off?

3. Disconnect the flying lead from hole number 22. Look carefully at each bulb. Has the situation altered?

4. Connect the flying lead from hole number 33 to hole number 27. Look carefully at each bulb. Is T_1 switched on or off? Is T_2 switched on or off?

5. Disconnect the flying lead from hole number 27. Look carefully at each bulb. Has the situation altered?

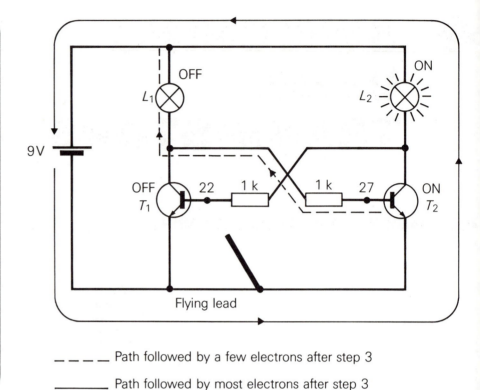

_ _ _ _ _ Path followed by a few electrons after step 3

_____ Path followed by most electrons after step 3

Figure 4.3   How Experiment 4.1 works.

How it works

When the flying lead is inserted into hole number 22 any current which may have been flowing in the base of T_1 now follows a much easier path. The electrons leave the negative terminal of the battery, flow through the flying lead, the 1 k resistor, bulb L_2 and so to the positive terminal of the battery. There is no flow of current in the base circuit of transistor T_1. It is therefore switched OFF and bulb L_1 does not glow.

A small current (too small to make a bulb glow) does flow through the base of transistor T_2 and through bulb L_1 (see Figure 4.3). Transistor T_2 is therefore switched ON. Current can therefore flow in the collector–emitter circuit of T_2 and so bulb L_2 glows. When the flying lead is removed the transistor which is switched ON remains ON and the transistor that is switched OFF remains OFF.

Explain, using a circuit diagram similar to the one shown in Figure 4.3, what happens when the flying lead is inserted in hole number 27.

Summary

From this experiment you ought to have discovered that:

When T_1 is switched ON	T_2 is switched OFF
When T_1 is switched OFF	T_2 is switched ON

Let us now have a look at three different types of switch which make use of this idea of one transistor controlling another.

4.2 THE BISTABLE SWITCH

The electric light switch shown in Figure 4.1 is an example of a *bistable switch*. The switch has two states, ON and OFF. Once put into either of these states the switch will remain there for as long as we want. So it is said to be 'bistable'.

The circuit described in Experiment 4.2 also has two stable states. It is an example of a bistable circuit or switch.

Experiment 4.2

To construct a bistable switch

APPARATUS: S-DeC; connecting wire; wire strippers; 0.06 A bulb; 9 V battery; 2 × transistors 2N3053; 3 × 1 k resistors (brown black red)

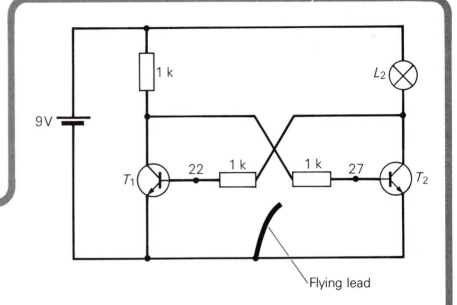

Figure 4.4 Circuit construction and diagram for Experiment 4.2.

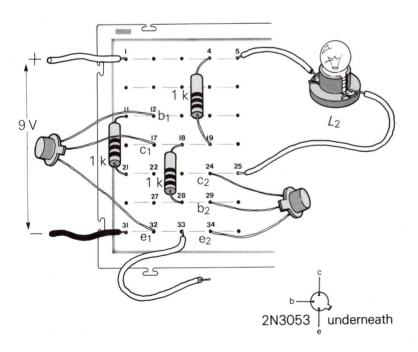

1. Set up the circuit as shown in Figure 4.4

2. Connect the flying lead from hole number 33 to hole number 22. Is bulb L_2 switched on or off?

3. Disconnect the flying lead from hole number 22. Is the bulb switched on or off?

4. Connect the flying lead from hole number 33 to hole number 27. Is the bulb switched on or off?

5. Disconnect the flying lead from hole number 27. Is the bulb switched on or off?

6. Now repeat steps 2, 3, 4 and 5. Check that your answers to the questions are still the same.

? How is this circuit similar to the electric switches in Figure 4.1?

How it works

When the flying lead is connected to hole number 22, almost no current flows in the base circuit of T_1. It is therefore switched OFF. As we saw in Experiment 4.1 if T_1 is switched OFF, T_2 is switched ON and bulb L_2 therefore glows. Even when the flying lead is removed bulb L_2 remains on showing that this condition is stable (see Figure 4.5a).

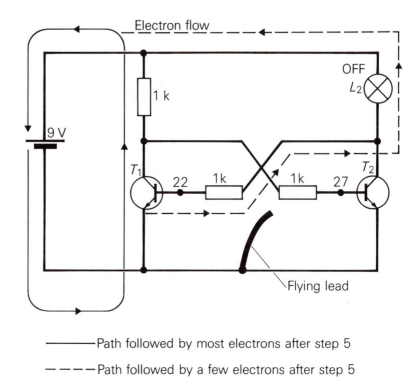

Electron flow

OFF

L_2

T_1

22   1k   1k   27

T_2

Flying lead

—————Path followed by most electrons after step 5

– – – – –Path followed by a few electrons after step 5

Figure 4.5(b)   The bulb is now switched off.

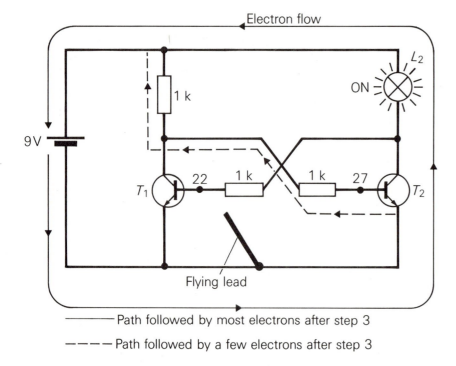

Electron flow

L_2

ON

1 k

9 V

T_1 22   1 k   1 k   27 T_2

Flying lead

—————Path followed by most electrons after step 3

– – – – –Path followed by a few electrons after step 3

Figure 4.5(a)   In this condition the bulb in the bistable circuit is on.

When the flying lead is connected to hole number 27, T_2 is switched OFF and bulb L_2 goes out. Once again the situation is stable and L_2 remains off even when the flying lead is removed from hole number 27. By alternately inserting the free end of the flying lead into holes 22 and 27, bulb L_2 can be switched on and off in exactly the same way the electric switch in Figure 4.1 switches lights on and off in the home (see Figure 4.5b).

Circuits like the one shown in Figure 4.4 which can be easily 'flipped' from one stable state and back again, are often called *flip-flop* circuits. A flip-flop circuit is used in Experiment 4.3.

Experiment 4.3

To build a magic light bulb

APPARATUS: S-DeC; connecting wire; wire strippers; 0.06 A bulb; 9 V battery; 2 × transistors 2N3053; LDR (ORP12); 3 × 1 k resistors (brown black red); 4k7 variable resistor; small shoebox; Sellotape

1. Set up the circuit as shown in Figure 4.6. Make sure that the connecting wires to the LDR and the bulb are quite long (20 to 25 cm).

2. Adjust the variable resistor until the bulb glows, then carefully readjust it until the bulb *just* goes out.

    Before the circuit is fixed permanently into its box, check that the adjustments made in step 2 are correct.

4. When this has been done put four holes in the lid of the shoebox (using a pencil).

5. Disconnect the LDR and the bulb from the S-DeC.

6. Thread the four connecting wires from the LDR and the bulb through the four holes.

7. Place the S-DeC and battery inside the shoebox.

8. Reconnect the four wires (correctly) to the S-DeC and replace the lid of the shoebox.

9. Sellotape the bulb holder and the LDR to the lid of the box so that:
    a) very little of the connecting wires can be seen
    b) the LDR and bulb are close together.

Now the fun begins

10. Go and find a friend and tell them that you have discovered a 'magic' bulb in the attic of your house.

11. Tell them to strike a match and light the bulb. Watch their face when not only does the bulb light up but it continues to glow when the match is removed.

12. After a while tell them that you do not want to 'waste' the bulb so you are going to blow it out. When you blow, be sure to blow from the side furthest away from the LDR. As you blow, 'cup' your hand around the bulb (just as you would a candle). If all goes well, when you stop the light from the bulb reaching the LDR the bulb should go out (see Figure 4.7).

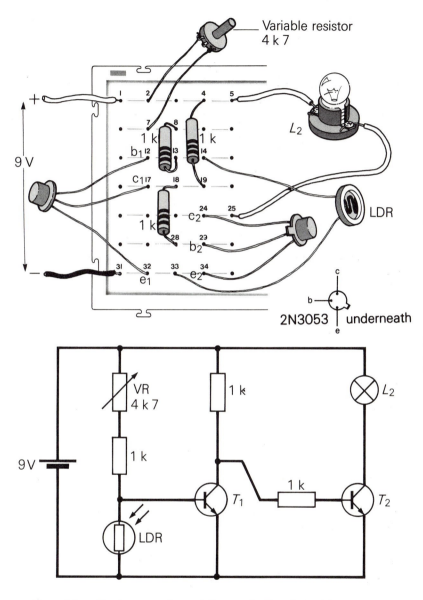

Figure 4.7   The magic bulb.

Figure 4.6   Circuit construction and diagram for Experiment 4.3.

3. Place the LDR next to the bulb. Strike a match and hold it just above the bulb. The bulb ought to glow *and* continue glowing when the lighted match is removed. If this is not the case then the value of the variable resistor must be altered until the circuit functions properly.

In Experiment 4.2 the transistor was switched on and off using a flying lead. What switches the transistor on and off in Experiment 4.3?

4.3 THE MONOSTABLE SWITCH

The bell-push shown in Figure 4.1 is a good example of a *monostable* switch. It has only one stable state, i.e. off. To switch the circuit on it is necessary to push the button in. But as soon as the button is released the switch returns to its more stable off state.

The circuit you will build in Experiment 4.4 also has only one stable state. It is a monostable circuit or switch.

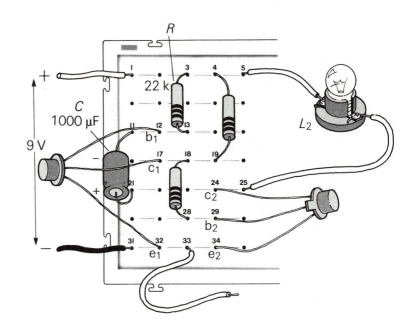

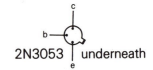

2N3053   underneath

Experiment 4.4

To construct a simple monostable switch

APPARATUS: S-DeC; connecting wire; wire strippers; 0.06 A bulb; 9 V battery; 2 × transistors 2N3053; 1000 μF capacitor; 2 × 1 k resistors (brown black red); 22 k resistor (red red orange)

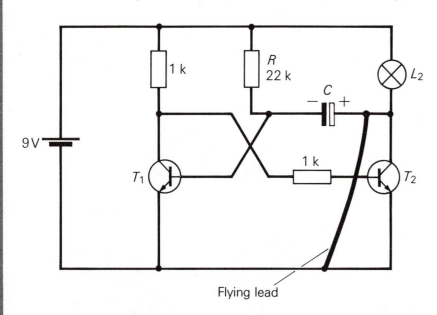

Figure 4.8   *Circuit construction and diagram for Experiment 4.4.*

1. Set up the circuit as shown in Figure 4.8.

2. Momentarily touch the loose end of the flying lead against the positive leg (hole number 21) of the capacitor. If the flying lead is kept in contact with the leg of the capacitor for longer than one second the circuit will not work. Describe precisely what happens to the bulb:

   a) When the flying lead is touched against the leg.

   b) After the flying lead has been removed.

3. Repeat step 2 several times and check that your observations are accurate.

   What is the stable state of this circuit?

ow it works

In experiment 3.4 we discovered that the switching on and off of a transistor can be delayed if a capacitor and resistor are included in the base circuit of the transistor. This two-transistor circuit uses the same idea.

When the flying lead is touched against the positive leg of the capacitor T_1 is switched off. T_2 is therefore switched on and the bulb L_2 glows. When the connection is broken T_1 is switched on but not straight away. It is delayed by the capacitor and resistor in its base circuit. T_2 therefore remains on and the bulb L_2 continues to glow.

Once the delay is over, T_1 is turned on, T_2 is turned off and the bulb goes out.

How long the bulb L_2 stays on after the flying lead has been removed depends upon the time it takes for the capacitor to become fully charged. This in turn depends upon:

1. The value of the capacitor – the larger this is the longer it will take to charge up.

2. The value of the resistor R through which the current has to flow – the larger this is the longer it will take to charge the capacitor fully.

By choosing the values of C and R carefully the circuit in Experiment 4.4 can be changed into an electronic timer.

xperiment 4.4a

To construct an electronic egg timer

APPARATUS: As Experiment 4.4 plus a selection of capacitors 100 µF to 2200 µF; resistors 1 k to 100 k; stop watch or clock

1. Set up the circuit as shown in Figure 4.8.

2. In your book draw a table similar to that shown here.

Capacitor (C)	Resistor (R)	No. of seconds the bulb is ON
1000 µF	22 k	20
470 µF	22 k	10

3. *Momentarily* touch the loose end of the flying lead against the positive leg of the capacitor and at the same instant start the stop watch.

4. When the bulb goes off, stop the stop watch.

5. In your table enter the values of the capacitor C, the resistor R and the length of time for which the bulb glowed.
(Two examples of the readings you should obtain have already been entered.)

6. Repeat the experiment with different values of C and R.

Using this simple circuit you ought to be able to adjust the values of C and R so that you can use the lighted bulb to measure accurately periods of time up to several minutes long.

To boil an egg just as you like it you will need to make a note of the values of C and R which caused the bulb to glow for: 180 seconds – if you like your egg very soft; approximately 260 seconds – if you like your egg medium soft.

Figure 4.9   The electronically timed egg.

? Estimate the value of the capacitor C and the resistor R you would need in order to time a hard boiled egg.

4.4 THE ASTABLE SWITCH

Figure 4.10 shows the kind of light often seen at a pelican crossing. When it is safe for pedestrians to use the crossing, a light glows green, but when the traffic lights are about to change and pedestrians must clear the crossing, the green light flashes on and off.

When the light is flashing it is probably being controlled by an *astable switching circuit.* This circuit, like the bistable and monostable circuits, has two states – ON and OFF – but this time *neither* of them is stable. The circuit continually changes from being on to being off to being on, etc.

Figure 4.10   A pelican crossing uses an astable switching circuit.

Experiment 4.5

To construct an astable switch (Flashing Lights)

APPARATUS: S-DeC; connecting wire; wire strippers; 2 × 0.06 A bulbs; 9 V battery; 2 × transistors 2N3053; 2 × 10 k resistors (brown black orange); 2 × 100 μF capacitors

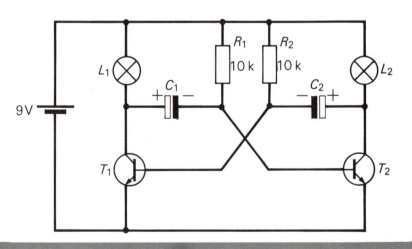

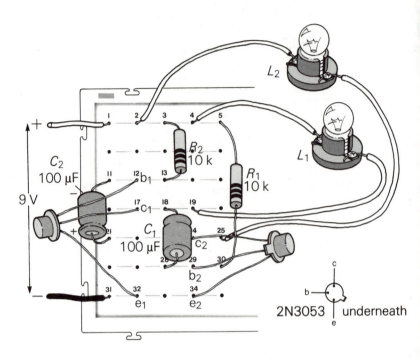

Figure 4.11   Circuit construction and diagram for Experiment 4.5.

1. Set up the circuit as shown in Figure 4.11. Look carefully at the two bulbs L_1 and L_2. Describe accurately how each bulb is behaving.

How it works

As we can see in Figure 4.11 an astable switch, or *multivibrator* it is sometimes called, consists of two monostable circuits connected together. The two bulbs L_1 and L_2 flash alternately showing that each transistor is being switched on and off by the charging and discharging of capacitors C_1 and C_2.

Whilst C_1 is charging up, T_2 is switched off and therefore T_1 and L_1 are switched on. When C_1 is fully charged, T_2 is switched on and C_2 then begins to charge up. T_1 is therefore switched off, bulb L_1 goes out and bulb L_2 comes on, and so on.

The rate at which the lamps flash on and off depends upon how quickly the two capacitors charge up and discharge.

xperiment 4.5a

To investigate the frequency of oscillation of an astable circuit

APPARATUS: As Experiment 4.5 plus 2 × 100 µF capacitors and 2 × 4k7 resistors (yellow violet red); 100 Ω resistor (brown black brown)

1. Set up the circuit as shown in Figure 4.11 but replace bulb L_1 with a 100 Ω resistor. Look carefully at the flashing bulb L_2. How rapidly is the light flashing (flashes/min)?
   Is the light a)   on longer than off?
               b)   off longer than on?
               c)   on and off for equal amounts of time?

2. Change the value of C_1 from 100 µF to 1000 µF. How does this affect the flashing light?

3. Return C_1 to its original value and change C_2 from 100 µF to 1000 µF. How does this affect the flashing light?

4. Return C_2 to its original value and change R_1 from 10 k to 4k7. How does this affect the flashing light?

5. Return R_1 to its original value and change R_2 from 10 k to 4k7. How does this affect the flashing light?

6. Now alter the circuit so that the value of both R_1 and R_2 is 4k7.

How does this affect the flashing light?

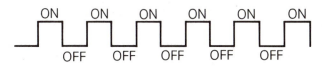

Figure 4.12   The changing state of bulb L_1.

Figure 4.12 shows how the state of bulb L_1 changes with time in step 1. Draw four more graphs showing how the state of bulb L_1 varied with time in steps 2, 3, 4, 5 and 6.

4.5 HIGH FREQUENCY OSCILLATORS

In Experiment 4.5 the values of C_1, C_2, R_1 and R_2 were such that the circuit oscillated from one state to the other fairly slowly (perhaps sixty times per minute). If we reduce the values of the components, the currents in the circuit will oscillate back and forth more rapidly, i.e. at a higher frequency. If the frequency of oscillation is very high, the bulbs L_1 and L_2 will no longer be able to flash on and off quickly enough to show that the circuit is switching back and forth. We must therefore find another means of detecting these oscillating currents.

When a current flows through a loudspeaker, a magnetic field is produced which causes the coil in the speaker to move. When the current stops flowing, the coil moves back to its original position. So if rapidly oscillating currents are passed through the speaker, the coil will be made to move back and forth rapidly, i.e. it will vibrate producing a note. A circuit capable of doing this is called a *high frequency oscillator.*

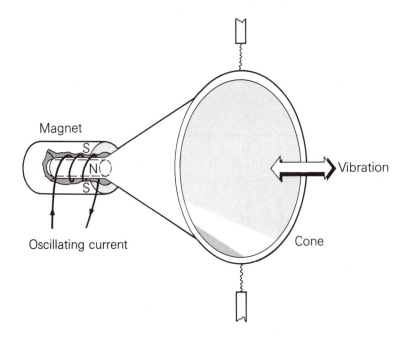

Figure 4.13   Construction of a loudspeaker.

Experiment 4.6

To build a high frequency oscillator

APPARATUS: S-DeC; connecting wire; wire strippers; 9 V battery; 2 × transistors 2N3053; 2 × 10 k resistors (brown black orange); 100 Ω resistor (brown black brown); 47 Ω variable resistor; 2 × 0.1 μF capacitors; low impedance loudspeaker

1. Set up the circuit as shown in Figure 4.14. Listen to the note produced by the speaker.

2. Adjust the variable resistor. What happens to the note produced by the speaker? Can you explain what is happening?

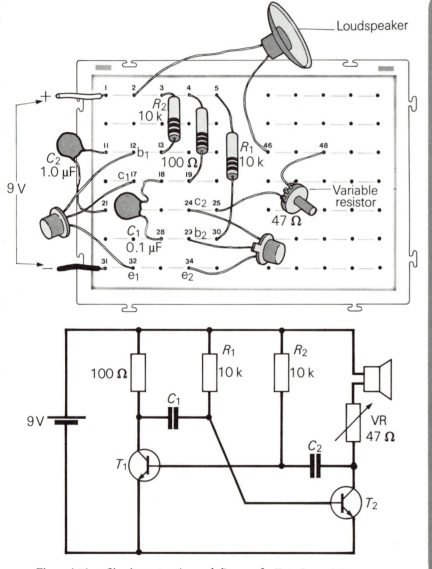

Figure 4.14   Circuit construction and diagram for Experiment 4.6.

Experiment 4.7

To build an audible burglar alarm

APPARATUS: S-DeC; connecting wire; wire strippers; 9 V battery; 2 × transistors 2N3053; 2 × 10 k resistors (brown black orange); 100 Ω resistor (brown black brown); 2 × 0.1 μF capacitors; low impedance loudspeaker; LDR (ORP 12)

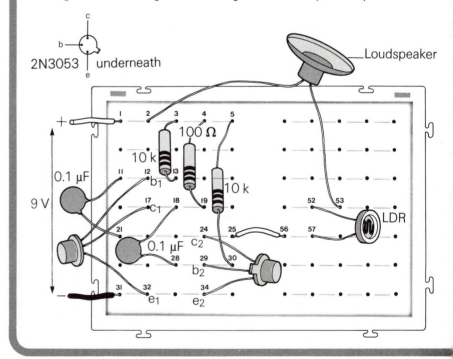

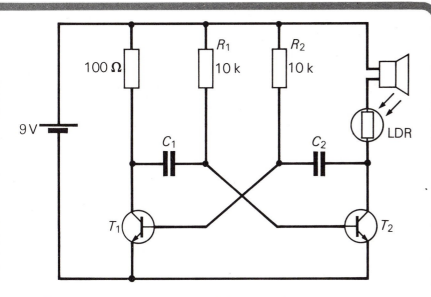

Figure 4.15   *Circuit construction and diagram for Experiment 4.7.*

1. Set up the circuit shown in Figure 4.15.
2. Cover the LDR with a cloth to block out all of the light.
3. Remove the cloth so that the light can now reach the LDR.

An astable circuit such as this could be used as a burglar alarm. If the burglar broke into your house at night and turned the lights on, the alarm would sound.

Figure 4.16   *The burglar alarm in operation.*

QUESTIONS ON CHAPTER 4

Write down the correct words to fill the gaps in these sentences.

1. A circuit which has one stable condition is known as a _____ circuit.

2. A circuit which has two stable conditions is known as a _____ circuit.

3. A circuit which has no stable conditions is known as an _____ circuit.

4. What are the advantages of using transistor switches in electrical circuits as opposed to mechanical switches such as those shown in Figure 4.1?

5. What are the two main components used in a 'timer' switch apart from the transistor?

```
R  E  S  T  N  E  T  I  M  J  T  Y
E  F  P  E  L  B  L  S  R  I  A  K
M  L  O  S  R  E  U  B  W  L  D  R
I  I  L  R  H  I  L  R  A  L  A  P
T  P  F  P  B  C  E  L  G  T  D  N
O  S  V  F  I  R  E  S  A  L  S  T
Q  U  E  V  M  O  L  G  F  R  A  A
E  N  E  L  B  A  T  S  I  B  A  R
T  R  O  T  A  L  L  I  C  S  O  P
```

There are nine different kinds of circuits and alarms hidden in the above word maze. The answers run in any direction: backwards, forwards, up, down and diagonally. Can you find them all?

(1) High frequency _____ .

(2) Neither state is stable.

(3) Both states are stable.

(4) Nickname for 3.

(5) You could use this kind of circuit instead of a stop watch.

(6) There are no branches in this kind of circuit.

(7) There are several different routes electrons can follow in this kind of circuit.

(8) This kind of alarm could prevent your house from being burnt down.

(9) This kind of alarm could prevent things being stolen from your house.

5 TRANSISTOR AMPLIFIERS

In Chapter 3 we discovered that a small change in the flow of electrons in the base circuit of a transistor would give rise to a much larger change in the flow of electrons in the collector–emitter circuit, i.e. the transistor is amplifying.

5.1 THE TRANSISTOR AS AN AMPLIFIER

An amplifier is something which magnifies or enlarges, just like the pantograph and convex lens shown in Figure 5.1.

5.2 THE SINGLE-STAGE AMPLIFIER

Experiment 5.1 demonstrates clearly how a transistor can be used as an amplifier.

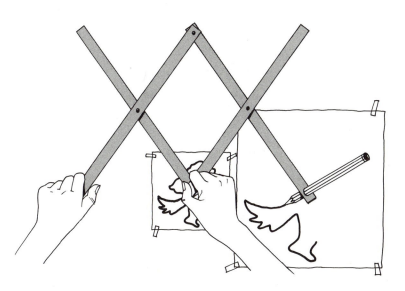

Figure 5.1   A pantograph and a lens demonstrate the process of amplification.

Experiment 5.1

To build a single-stage amplifier

APPARATUS: S-DeC; connecting wire; wire strippers; 9 V battery; 1 × transistor 2N3053; 33 k resistor (orange orange orange); 2 × magnetic headphones (300 Ω); 100 μF capacitor

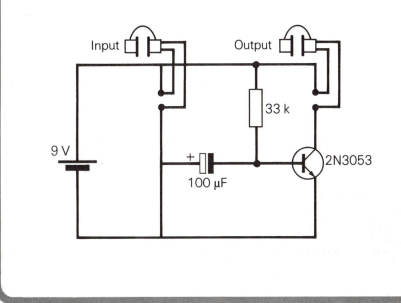

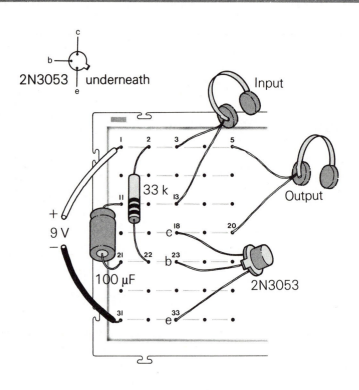

Figure 5.2   *Circuit construction and diagram for Experiment 5.1.*

1. Set up the circuit as shown in Figure 5.2.

2. Ask a friend to put on the headphones connected to holes number 5 and 20.

3. Gently tap or speak into the headphones/microphone connected to holes number 3 and 13. Can your friend hear anything?

How it works

When someone speaks into the headphones/microphone, the current entering the base of the transistor changes. The transistor amplifies this change producing a similar but much larger current in the collector-emitter circuit (see Figure 5.3). This in turn produces a sound in the second set of headphones. A circuit such as this is known as a *single-stage amplifier* because it contains just one transistor.

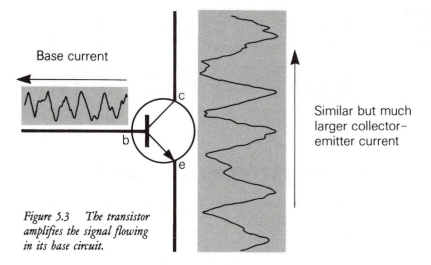

Figure 5.3   *The transistor amplifies the signal flowing in its base circuit.*

In Experiment 5.1 it is possible for only one person to speak and the other to listen. A two-way conversation is not possible. In Experiment 5.2 the circuit is modified to allow a two-way conversation.

Experiment 5.2

To build a two-way intercom

APPARATUS: As Experiment 5.1 plus 1 double pole switch

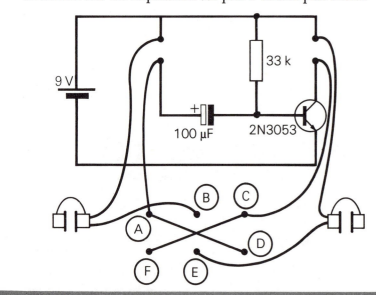

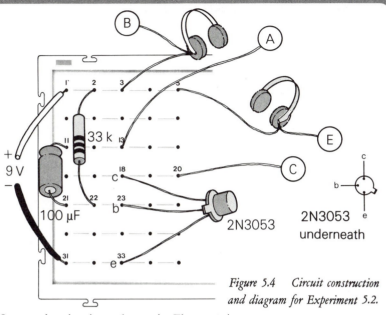

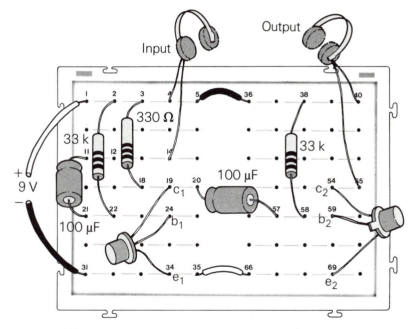

5.3 TWO-STAGE AMPLIFIER

The amplified sound obtained in Experiments 5.1 and 5.2 may be rather weak. Much better amplification is obtained if two transistors are included in the circuit.

Experiment 5.3

To build a two-stage amplifier

APPARATUS: S-DeC; connecting wire; wire strippers; 2 × transistors 2N3053; 2 × 33 k resistors (orange orange orange) 1 × 330 Ω (orange orange brown); 2 × magnetic headphones (300 Ω); 2 × 100 µF capacitors

Figure 5.4   Circuit construction and diagram for Experiment 5.2.

1. Set up the circuit as shown in Figure 5.4.
2. Ask a friend to put on the headphones.
3. Make sure that the double pole switch has been closed so that your friend can hear when you speak into your headphones.
4. Put on your headphones and move the double pole switch over to the other side. If your friend now taps or speaks into their headphones, you should be able to hear them through your headphones.

[?] When people such as aeroplane pilots or ships' captains talk to each other on the radio, they often use phrases such as 'over' or 'over and out'. What do these phrases mean and why are they important? (Hint: What did you have to do in Experiment 5.2 when you stopped speaking and then wanted to listen?)

Figure 5.5   Ship's radio operator.

Figure 5.6

1. Set up the circuit as shown in Figure 5.6.
2. Ask a friend to put on the headphones connected to hole numbers 40 and 55.
3. Gently tap or speak into the headphones/microphone connected to hole numbers 4 and 14. What can your friend hear?

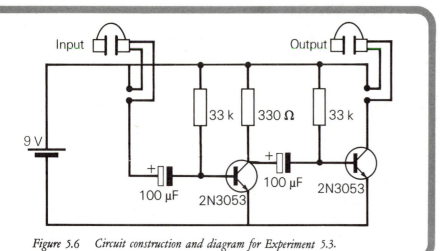

Figure 5.6   Circuit construction and diagram for Experiment 5.3.

How it works

When someone speaks into the headphones a small 'changing' current flows in the base circuit of T_1. This is amplified by T_1 and then fed into the base circuit of T_2. Transistor T_2 now amplifies this producing an even larger current in the collector–emitter circuit.

If you discover that the output from this two-stage amplifier is very loud and distorted, this is probably because you have too much amplification. To solve this problem you need to introduce a volume control into the circuit.

? What type of component would you choose for your volume control and where in the circuit would you include it?

(Hint! the size of the current flowing in the base circuit of each transistor controls the collector–emitter current.)

Figure 5.7   Control desk in a modern sound recording studio.

5.4 INCREASED SENSITIVITY

We know from Experiments 5.1, 5.2 and 5.3 that small changes in current can be amplified using one or more transistors. So it ought to be possible to use transistors to increase the sensitivity of circuits containing components such as thermistors, light dependent resistors, etc.

In Experiment 1.9 a circuit was built which could be used as a fire alarm. One of the problems with the circuit was that the thermistor had to be very hot before the bulb glowed. In Experiment 3.3 an improved fire alarm was constructed which included a transistor in the circuit. This amplified the changes in the thermistor circuit; making the alarm more sensitive. An even more sensitive circuit can be built using two transistors.

Experiment 5.4

To build a temperature sensitive circuit

APPARATUS: S-DeC; connecting wire; wire strippers; 0.06 A bulb; 9 V battery; 2 × transistors 2N3053; 3 × 1 k resistors (brown black red); 4k7 variable resistor; thermistor (TH3)

1.   Set up the circuit as shown in Figure 5.8.

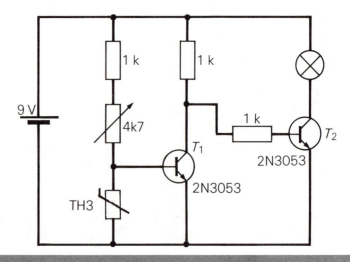

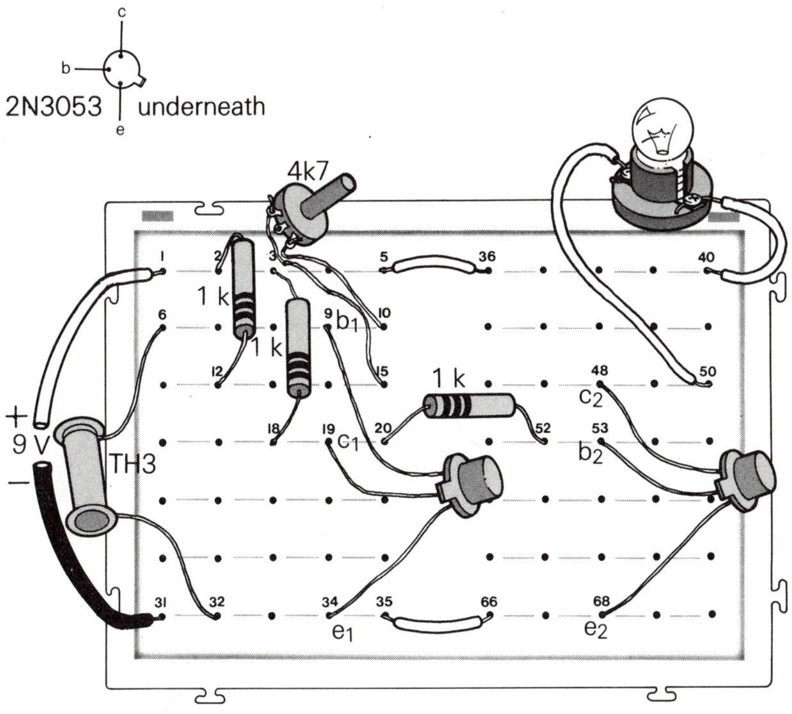

c
b
2N3053 underneath
e
4k7
1 k
1 k
1 k
+
9 V
–
TH3
b1
c1
c2
b2
e1
e2

Figure 5.8 Circuit construction and diagram for Experiment 5.4.

2. Adjust the variable resistor so that the bulb is glowing, and then readjust it so that the bulb *just* goes out.

3. Warm the thermistor up by closing your hand around it. What happens to the bulb?

4. Take your hand away from the thermistor. What happens to the bulb after a few seconds? Explain why this circuit is more sensitive.

5. Adjust the variable resistor a small amount so that the bulb just fails to glow when the thermistor is warmed by your hand. Now warm the thermistor a little more using a match. What happens to the bulb?

What does the variable resistor control?

Experiment 5.5.

To build a sensitive parking light

APPARATUS: S-DeC; connecting wire; wire strippers; 0.06 A bulb; 9 V battery; 2 × transistors 2N3053; 2 × 1 k resistors (brown black red); 4k7 variable resistor; LDR (ORP 12)

ORP 12
+
9 V
–
4.7 k
1 k
1 k
b1
c1
c2
b2
e1
e2
ORP 12
1 k
1 k
9 V
2N3053
T_2
2N3053
T_1
4k7

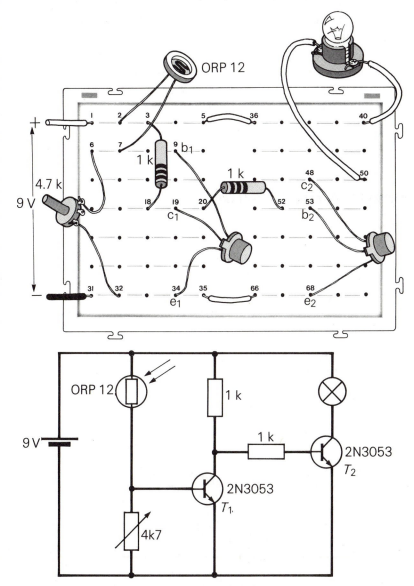

Figure 5.9 Circuit construction and diagram for Experiment 5.5.

1. Repeat Experiments 1.10 and 3.2. How sensitive are these circuits?

2. Now construct the circuit shown in Figure 5.9.

3. Adjust the variable resistor so that the bulb is glowing, and then readjust it so that the bulb *just* goes out.

4. Discover where most of the light is coming from, e.g. a window or electric light. Then block off some of this light by simply holding a book between your circuit and the light source. What happens to the light bulb?

5. Adjust the variable resistor a small amount so that the bulb does not glow when a little of the light is blocked off. Now block off more of the light. What happens to the bulb? What does the variable resistor control?

CHAPTER 5 QUESTIONS

1. What exactly does an amplifier do?

2. What is the difference between a one-stage amplifier and a two-stage amplifier?

3. What extra piece of equipment is needed in order to change a two-stage amplifier into a two-way intercom? How is this piece of equipment used?

4. Explain why an automatic parking light circuit which includes two transistors (Experiment 5.5) is more sensitive than a circuit which contains just one transistor.

CROSSWORD ON CHAPTER 5

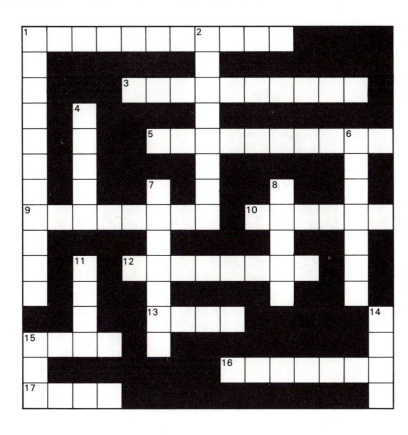

Across

1 Additional transistors in an amplifier improve the circuit's _____ . (11)

3 A device which converts sound to a varying current. (10)

5 A pair of _____ convert a varying current into sound. (10)

9 A _____ amplifier contains two transistors. (3, 5)

10 A small _____ can be amplified using transistors. (6)

12 Two-way conversation is possible using this. (8)

13 This type of alarm is sensitive to changes of temperature. (4)

15 The words '_____ and 15 down' are used to close a two-way conversation. (4)

16 A ship's _____ often uses expressions such as 15 across and 15 down. (7)

17 A 12 across enables people to _____ to each other. (4)

Down

1 A _____ amplifier uses only one transistor. (6, 5)

2 The value of a _____ resistor is adjustable. (8)

4 Aircraft pilots keep in touch by _____ . (5)

6 Another word for 'amplify'. (7)

7 Yet another word for 'amplify'. (7)

8 He talks to his ground-controller using the 4 down. (5)

11 A small signal requiring amplification is fed into the _____ of a transistor. (4)

14 A kind of amplifier _____ (4)

15 '15 across and _____' indicates the end of a two-way conversation. (3)

6 ELECTRONIC SYSTEMS

6.1 THE SYSTEMS APPROACH

The singer in the pop group shown in Figure 6.1 probably knows that the equipment he is using contains large numbers of electronic components. But it is unlikely that he could explain precisely what each component does. For the singer, all that is important is that he knows the overall functions of certain groups of components. He needs to know what a microphone is and how to use it. He needs to know what an amplifier is and perhaps how to set it up in order to get the particular sound he wants. He also needs to know which of the 'boxes' contain speakers and the kinds of sounds these should be producing.

Figure 6.1   Pop groups use electronic equipment. They need to know how the system works but not the function of each component within the 'boxes'.

When the equipment is all connected together it forms an *electronic system*. In this particular example the singer and the rest of the group are using 'amplification systems' (see Figure 6.2).

Figure 6.2   There can be clear advantages to the systems approach.

'Block diagrams' are often used to explain electronic systems. At their simplest, most systems can be represented by three or four basic blocks (see Figure 6.3).

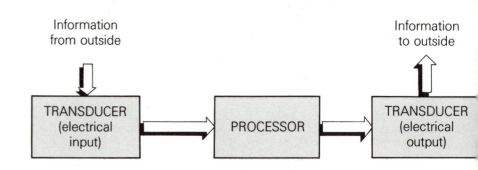

Figure 6.3   Example of a block diagram.

The information which the *processor* in the centre of these systems is handling, must be in the form of an electric current or voltage. In order to change information into this form input devices are used such as microphones, thermistors, light dependent resistors, etc. Devices such as these are called *transducers*.

When the information has been processed, it needs to be changed back into a form that we human beings can handle. To do this transducers are again used, such as loudspeakers, bulbs, bells, etc.

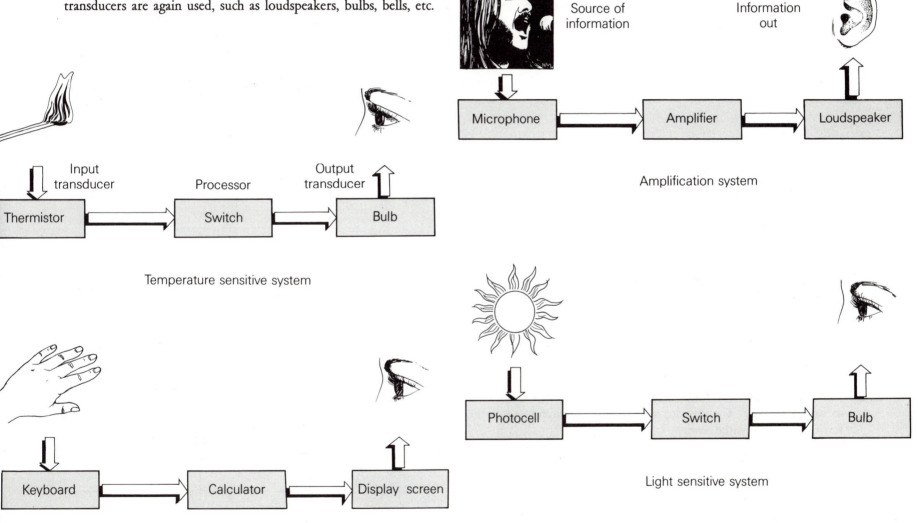

Figure 6.4   Block diagrams showing how information can be processed in some common electronic systems.

6.2 A RADIO

Experiment 6.1

To build a simple radio receiver

APPARATUS: S-DeC; connecting wire; wire strippers; diode 0A91; crystal earpiece; 220 pF capacitor; ferrite rod; 2 m enamelled copper wire, 24 swg; length of wire at least 5 m long; knife or file

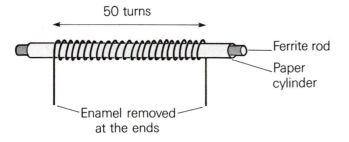

Figure 6.5   *Construction of the ferrite rod aerial.*

1. Take a piece of paper and wrap it around the ferrite rod several times to form a cylinder. The cylinder must be loose enough to allow the ferrite rod to be withdrawn.

2. Wrap the enamelled wire around the rod and cylinder 50 times. Be careful not to wrap the wire too tightly. You should still be able to move the ferrite rod.

3. Using a knife or file remove some of the insulating enamel from both ends of the copper wire.

4. Set up the circuit as shown in Figure 6.6.

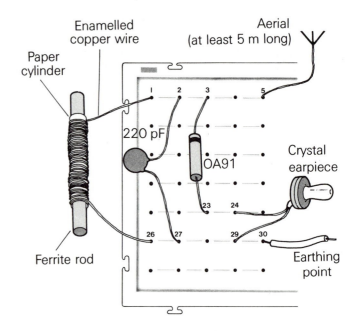

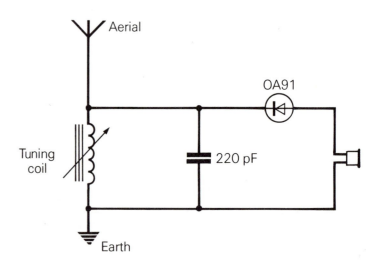

Figure 6.6   *Circuit construction and diagram for Experiment 6.1.*

5. Stretch the 5 m of aerial wire across the room. If your teacher will allow you to do so, dangle the wire out of the window.

6. In areas where radio reception is poor it is often crucial to have a 'good earth'. A metal water tap (*not* plastic coated) should make an excellent earthing point (see Figure 6.7).

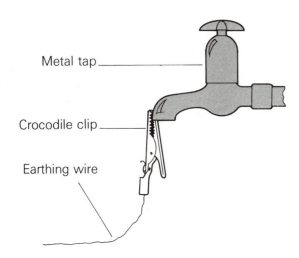

Figure 6.7   An earth connection can be made to a metal water tap.

7. When the circuit is complete, put the crystal earpiece in your ear and gradually move the ferrite rod in and out of the copper coil until you can hear a radio station. This is called *tuning* the circuit (see Figure 6.8).

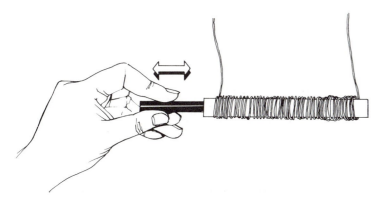

Figure 6.8   Tuning a radio receiver by moving the ferrite rod in and out of the copper coil.

At the end of Experiment 6.1 you should have a simple radio receiver which can detect or can be tuned into at least one radio station. What is now needed, in order to improve your listening, is to amplify the signals your set is receiving.

Experiment 6.2

To build a 'complete' radio (receiver and amplifier)

APPARATUS: As Experiment 6.1 plus 9 V battery; 0.1 μF capacitor; 100 k resistor (brown black yellow); crystal earpiece; transistor 2N3053

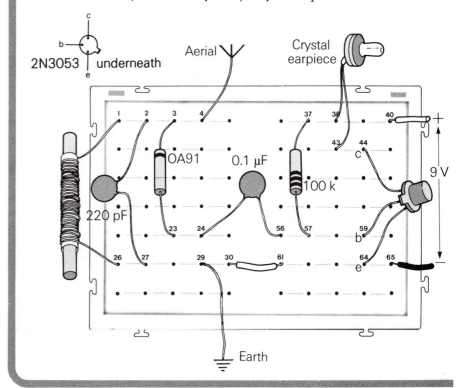

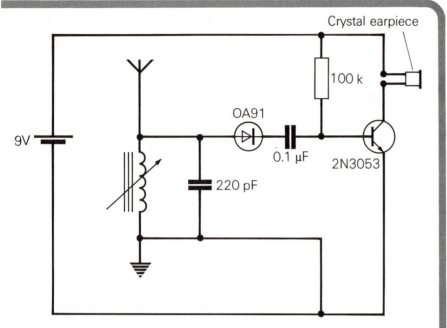

Figure 6.9   *Circuit construction and diagram for Experiment 6.2.*

1. Set up the circuit as shown in Figure 6.9.
2. Put the crystal earpiece in your ear and again gradually move the ferrite rod back and forth until you can hear a radio station.

The signal you hear now should be much stronger.

How it works

Figure 6.10   *Pupils using the simple intercom.*

If the boy in Figure 6.10 wants to talk to his friend in the next room, he could do so by using a simple intercom similar to the one you built in Experiment 5.3.

But if the pilot of an aeroplane wants to talk to the control tower he must use a radio.

Figure 6.11   *A radio link between control tower and pilot is essential.*

When an intercom is used as in Figure 6.10 the messages are carried through wires. When radio is used, the messages are carried through the air by waves – *radio waves*.

These waves and the messages they carry can travel hundreds and thousands of kilometres. Indeed if we want to speak to someone on the other side of the world, we can do so by bouncing the radio waves off a communications satellite.

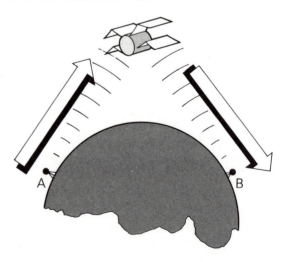

Figure 6.12   *Satellite communication means that radio signals can be transmitted around the world.*

To communicate by radio, two pieces of apparatus are needed. The person sending the message must have a *transmitter* and the person waiting to hear the message must have a *receiver*.

The transmitter

In a radio transmitter, the waves created by speaking into a microphone (i.e. the message) are added to (superimposed on) radio carrier waves.

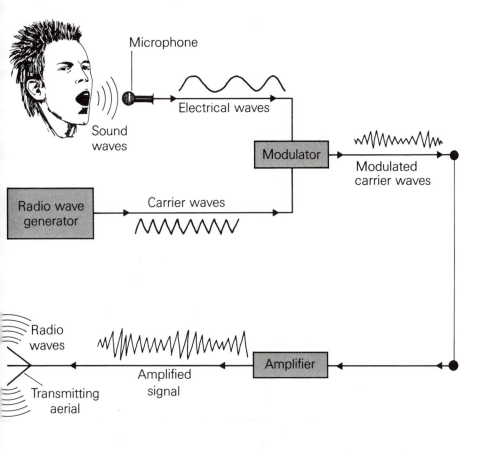

Figure 6.13   The basic elements of a radio transmitter.

The resultant waves are called *modulated carrier waves*. These modulated waves are then amplified and transmitted as radio waves using a transmitting aerial.

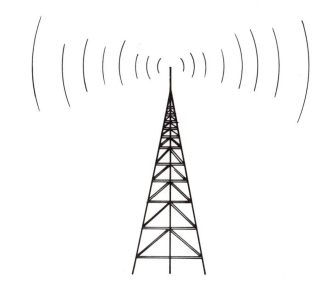

Figure 6.14   A radio transmitting aerial.

The receiver

When the receiver has been tuned in to a particular transmitter, radio waves pass through the receiving aerial and create modulated waves similar to those produced within the transmitter.

These waves are amplified and then *demodulated* by a detector, and the message itself is amplified a second time, and fed into an earphone or a loudspeaker. (See Figure 6.15.)

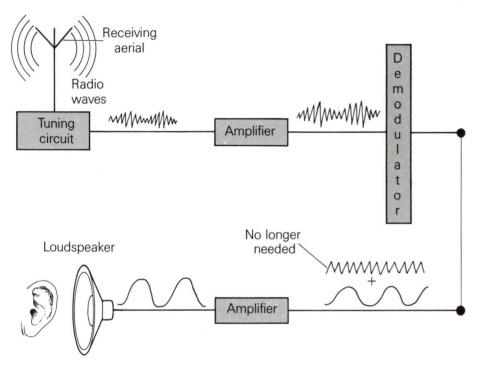

Figure 6.15   The basic elements of a radio receiver.

Figure 6.16   Reel to reel tape recorder.

1. Recording on tape

The tape used in tape recording is usually made of fairly tough b
flexible plastic which has been coated with a thin film of iron oxi
or chromium oxide particles.

6.3 A TAPE RECORDER

How it works

Most tape recorders have two basic functions:

1. They record or store information on tape.
2. They can replay the information stored.

Figure 6.17(a)   Recording a signal on magnetic tape.

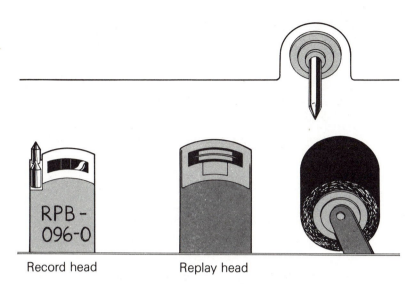

Record head   Replay head

Figure 6.17(b)   *The record and replay heads on a modern tape recorder.*

As this tape passes a small electromagnet inside the recording-head, the metal oxide particles are magnetised to form small permanent magnets.

If the signal that is being recorded has a low frequency, these magnets are well spaced out. If the signal has a high frequency they are much closer together.

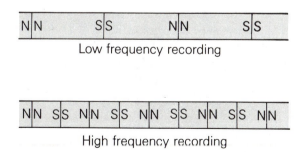

Low frequency recording

High frequency recording

Figure 6.18   *Small permanent magnets form on the tape when a signal is recorded.*

2. Replaying the tape

When the tape is played back, the reverse process occurs. As the permanent magnets on the tape pass the replay-head, a changing electric current is generated. It is identical to the signal that was initially fed into the tape recorder. This current is then amplified and the signal is passed out through a loudspeaker.

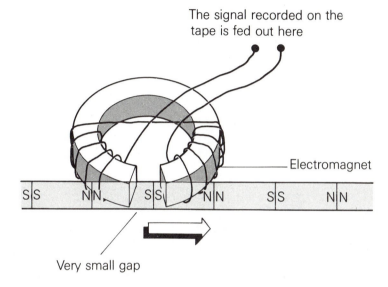

The signal recorded on the tape is fed out here

Electromagnet

Very small gap

Figure 6.19   *Replaying a signal that has been recorded on magnetic tape.*

6.4 A RECORD PLAYER

How it works

As the disc rotates on the turntable, the stylus or needle spirals inwards following the groove. This groove is not smooth and so the stylus is continuously being moved from side to side and up and down. These movements are 'picked up' by the cartridge immediately above the stylus and are converted into an electrical signal. This is then amplified and fed into loudspeakers or headphones.

A modern record reproduction system

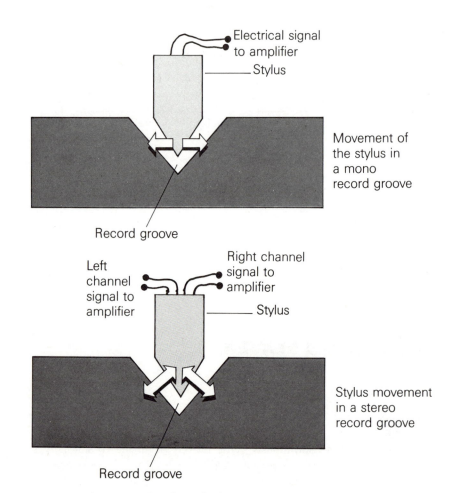

Figure 6.20   *Sound reproduction systems.*

CHAPTER 6 QUESTIONS

1. Suggest one reason why most people use the syste
    approach to electrical/electronic equipment in the home.

2. How can an electronic system be most easily represented

3. What is a transducer? Name four such devices.

4. What is the main difference between a crystal set and a 'co
    plete' radio?

5. How do radio messages travel through the 'air'?

6. What is needed to 'broadcast' radio signals?

7. What is needed to 'gather in' radio signals?

8. Explain how it is possible to speak, using a radio, to some
    on the opposite side of the world. Include a diagram in y
    explanation.

9. Explain the meaning of the following phrases:
    a) Carrier Wave
    b) Modulated Carrier Wave
    c) Demodulated Wave

10. a) Most recording tapes are made of plastic but with w
        have they been coated?
    b) What happens when a tape passes close to the record
        head if a signal is being fed into it?
    c) If the frequency of the signal being fed into the record
        head gradually increases how does this affect the ta

11. Draw a simple 'block' diagram to represent a tape record
    being used to replay a signal already stored on a piece of ta

12. Draw a simple 'block' diagram to represent a record play

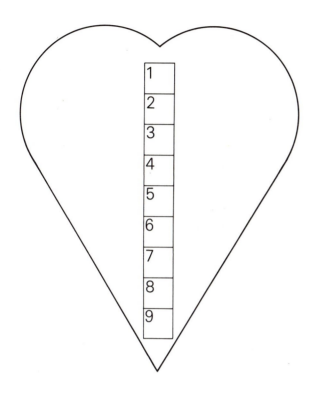

The first letter of each of these answers will tell you what is always at the heart of a system.

Hard Clues

(1) What do members of a football or cricket team do.

(2) I usually catch fish with mine.

(3) Where you might be going when you have finished talking on the radio.

(4) Loaded into a shotgun or given a bumpy ride on a record.

(5) The source of attraction in a tape recorder?

(6) This kind of approach to electronics is much easier.

(7) To change from being on to being off.

(8) What eventually emerges from the second transducer.

(9) The one who gets it.

Easy Clues

(1) What you must do with a record if you want to hear it.

(2) You have a ferrite one of these in your radio.

(3) What you say when you have finished talking on a radio transmitter.

(4) The transducer on a record player.

(5) The special kind of magnet used in a tape recorder.

(6) What this chapter is all about.

(7) Used for turning the circuit on and off.

(8) No, not the input – the other one.

(9) What you need to 'pick up' radio waves.

7 ANALOG AND DIGITAL ELECTRONICS

7.1 CONTINUOUS AND NON-CONTINUOUS SYSTEMS

Look carefully at the two clocks in Figure 7.1.

Although both clocks tell us the time, they do so in two completely different ways.

The clock in Figure 7.1a is a traditional mechanical or 'wind up' clock. As the cogs and wheels behind the clockface turn continuously, so do the minute and hour hands. The time displayed is continuous.

Figure 7.1(a)   Traditional mechanical clock.

The clock in Figure 7.1b is completely different. It is a digital clo... We know precisely what time it is when the numbers or digits ... changing. But between the changing of one digit to the changing ... the next we do not. The time displayed is non-continuous.

Figure 7.1(b)   A digital clock.

Electronic systems, like these clocks, can work in a continuous o... non-continuous manner. Those that work in a continuous way ... called *analog* systems. Those that work in a non-continuous way ... called *digital* systems.

7.2 EXAMPLES OF ANALOG SYSTEMS

The system shown in Figure 7.2 is an analog system. The pup... speech is carried by sound waves to the microphone where it is c... verted into electrical waves. These electrical waves are then amplif... and finally converted back to sound waves by the loudspeak... Throughout the system the changes are continuous.

When a transistor is being used as an amplifier it is part of ... *analog system.*

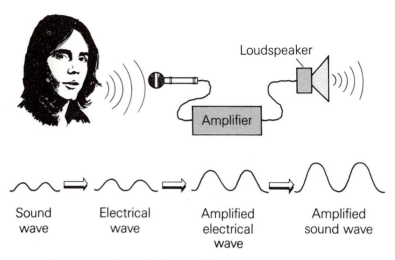

Sound wave   Electrical wave   Amplified electrical wave   Amplified sound wave

Figure 7.2   Example of an analog system.

The waves before and after amplification are continuous (see Figure 7.3).

The circuit shown in Figure 7.4 is also an analog circuit. As the value of the variable resistor is altered, the brightness of the bulb alters. Once again all changes are continuous.

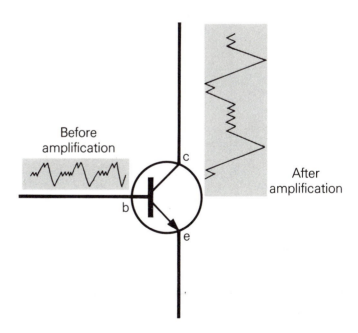

Before amplification

After amplification

Figure 7.3   Electrical wave before and after amplification.

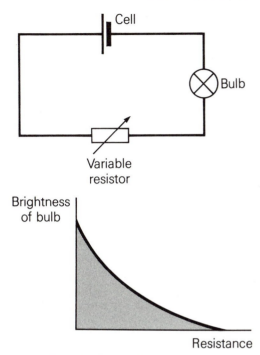

Cell

Bulb

Variable resistor

Brightness of bulb

Resistance

Figure 7.4   Example of an analog circuit.

7.3 EXAMPLES OF DIGITAL SYSTEMS

In a digital system the information being handled is *not* continuous.

The boy in Figure 7.5 is carrying out an experiment in which he needs to measure the temperature of the water in the beaker every five minutes. The following table shows the results he obtained.

Figure 7.5   An experiment which produces 'non-continuous' results.

Time (min.)	Temperature (°C)
0	5
5	25
10	45
15	60
20	75

The information in this table is not continuous. We don't know, for example, what the temperature of the water was after three minutes or after eight minutes. We only know the temperature of the water at five minute intervals. So we need to introduce this information into a digital system which deals with individual numbers rather than continuously changing values.

The circuit shown in Figure 7.6 is a *digital* circuit. The variable resistor cannot be altered continuously, only in steps. The brightness of the bulb must therefore change in steps.

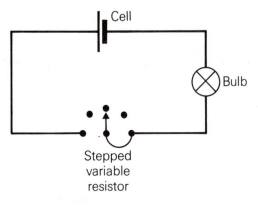

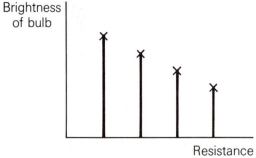

Figure 7.6   Example of a digital circuit.

? Which of the following could be included in an analog system?
a) The cartridge and stylus from a record player
b) The electromagnet inside the recording-head of a tape record
c) The moving hands of an electric clock.

7.4 BINARY DIGITS (NUMBER CODE)

Digital processors such as computers handle information and perform calculations using a number system called *binary*. Instead of using ten different digits 0, 1, 2, 3, 4, 5, 6, 7, 8, 9, as we do everyday life, computers use just two digits, 0 and 1. The table below shows how this is done.

4-Digit Binary Table

Number	Binary Number
0	0 0 0 0
1	0 0 0 1
2	0 0 1 0
3	0 0 1 1
4	0 1 0 0
5	0 1 0 1
6	0 1 1 0
7	0 1 1 1
8	1 0 0 0
9	1 0 0 1
10	1 0 1 0
11	1 0 1 1
12	1 1 0 0
13	1 1 0 1
14	1 1 1 0
15	1 1 1 1

In Experiment 8.1 you will actually build a four-digit binary counter using a component called an *integrated circuit*. But before this we can explain very simply how the counter works by using block diagrams (see Figure 7.7).

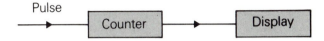

Figure 7.7   Block diagram of a simple counter system.

The counter is adding together the total number of pulses put into the system and is then displaying this number in binary code (see the table on p. 66).

The display consists of four light emitting diodes placed side by side. If the counter is empty, i.e. no pulses have been fed into the system, none of the LEDs will glow.

If we introduce one pulse into the counter, the display will look like Figure 7.8a.

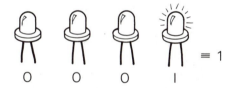

Figure 7.8(a)

If we add two more pulses, the display will look like Figure 7.8b.

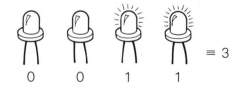

Figure 7.8(b)

[?] How many pulses have been introduced into the system if the LEDs look like Figure 7.8c?

Figure 7.8(c)

Digital circuits which handle numbers in this way can also be used to handle other types of information which have only two states. For example:

Yes – No	Left – Right
High – Low	True – False

In fact digital circuits can be used to handle any kind of information, provided it can be written in binary code.

7.5 LOGIC GATES

THE AND GATE

In electronics, circuits are often used which contain arrangements of switches called *logic gates*.

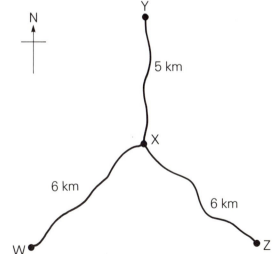

Figure 7.9   There is a logical sequence in the process of using a map.

Look at the three statements below:

1. If I lived at X
2. If I drove 5 km northwards
3. I would arrive at Y.

These three statements, when compared with the map in Figure 7.9 'make sense', i.e. statement 3 *logically* follows on from statements 1 and 2.

We can represent this situation electrically by using switches to represent the three statements.

If a switch is closed, this means that a statement is true.

If a switch is open, this means a statement is untrue.

If there is an output from the circuit, i.e. a bulb glows, this means that the conclusion drawn from statements 1 and 2 is logical and true.

The electrical circuit in Figure 7.10 can be used to represent our three statements. If X is closed and Y is closed then L will glow. The two pieces of information (inputs) when 'true' produce an output (a glowing bulb).

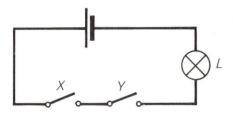

Figure 7.10   This circuit can be used to represent the three logic statements above.

We can represent all possible situations and their end results in a truth table. In such a table we use a '0' to show that there is *no* output or input (false statement) and a '1' to show that there *is* an output or input (true statement).

The table below is the truth table for the circuit in Figure 7.10.

Input X	Input Y	Output
0	0	0
1	0	0
0	1	0
1	1	1

The first row of the table states that if both switches X and Y are open, bulb L will not glow. Check the condition for each of the remaining rows. Do you agree with each conclusion? A logic gate which behaves as the above truth table predicts is known as an *AND* gate because unless X AND Y are both true (i.e. are closed) then there is no output.

Why are truth tables and logic gates important? What possible use could they be?

Look at the lift shown in Figure 7.11. It is a manual lift. Its doors do not open and close automatically. On entering the lift, one door must be closed AND then the other door must be closed if the lift is to work. If either door is open the lift will not operate. The electronic circuit which controls the lift will contain an AND gate similar to that shown in Figure 7.10.

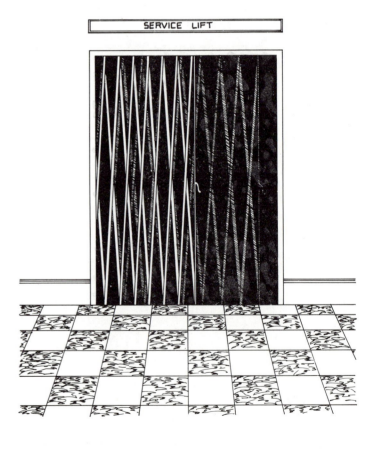

Figure 7.11   Manual lift with two doors.

Figure 7.12   *Symbol used for an AND gate.*

Let us have a look at several other kinds of logic gates and their uses.

THE OR GATE

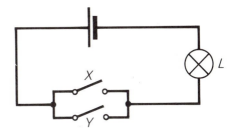

Figure 7.13   *This circuit will produce the logic of an OR gate.*

Look at Figure 7.13. This is a kind of *OR* Gate. If *X* OR *Y* is true (i.e. closed) the bulb *L* glows.

Input X	Input Y	Output L
0	0	0
1	0	1
0	1	1
1	1	1

Explain each of the conditions described in the above table using the circuit shown in Figure 7.13.

When we approach a level crossing, if there is a train coming from the left OR from the right, the red light will begin to flash, and the barriers will be lowered. This circuitry is controlled by an OR gate.

Figure 7.14   *The warning lights at a level crossing are controlled by an OR gate.*

Figure 7.15 shows the diagrammatic form of an OR gate.

Figure 7.15   *Symbol used for an OR gate.*

NOT GATE

Look at Figure 7.16. This is a kind of *not* gate. If there is NOT a current flowing around the electromagnet, switch X is closed by the spring and the bulb glows.

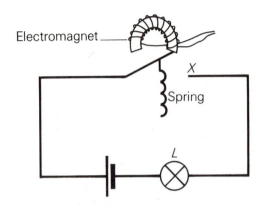

Figure 7.16   A circuit that produces a NOT gate.

The truth table for the circuit in Figure 7.16 is shown below.

Input	Output
1	0
0	1

In a simple automatic parking light similar to that built in Experiment 3.2, the circuit is controlled by a kind of NOT gate. If there is NOT enough light reaching the LDR the bulb glows.

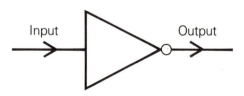

Figure 7.17   Symbol used for a NOT gate.

NAND GATE

If we add a NOT gate to an AND gate, we produce a *NAND* (i. NOT AND) gate.

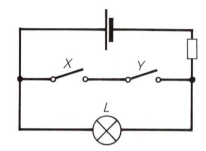

Figure 7.18   Circuit that produces a NAND gate.

Look at Figure 7.18. This is a kind of NAND gate. If switch X i closed AND the switch Y is closed, the bulb L does NOT glow.

The truth table for the circuit in Figure 7.18 is shown below.

Input X	Input Y	Output
0	0	1
0	1	1
1	0	1
1	1	0

The driver in Figure 7.19 must NOT leave his seat belt unfastened AND his passenger must NOT leave her seat belt unfastened. If one or both of them does, the warning light will come on.

Figure 7.19   The seat belt warning light is controlled by a NAND gate.

Figure 7.20   Symbol used for a NAND gate.

Figure 7.22   Symbol for a NOR gate.

[?] Try to discover a practical application for a NOR gate. Be sure to check that all the conditions stated in the truth table are fulfilled.

[?] Nowadays we do not use mechanical switches to build logic gates, instead we use _____ .

NOR GATE

If we add a NOT gate to an OR gate we produce a *NOR* gate.

Look at Figure 7.21. This is a kind of NOR gate. If switch *X* is NOT closed, NOR switch *Y,* the bulb *L* glows.

QUESTIONS ON CHAPTER 7

Write down the correct words to fill the gaps in these sentences:

1. In a digital system the information being handled is _____ .

2. In an analog system the information being handled is _____ .

3. The binary numbering system uses just _____ digits.

4. Logic gates are arrangements of _____ .

5. If we add a NOT gate to an OR gate, we produce a _____ gate.

6. If we add a NOT gate to an AND gate, we produce a _____ gate.

7. Copy the table below and fill in the missing spaces:

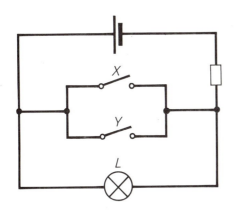

Figure 7.21   Circuit for a NOR gate.

The truth table for a NOR gate is shown below.

Input X	Input Y	Output
0	0	1
0	1	0
1	0	0
1	1	0

Number	Binary Number
8	
22	
30	
	101
	1111
	10000
	1011

8. Which of the following can *easily* be represented in binary.

    Up/Down
    North/South/East/West
    Yes/No
    Open/Closed
    Monday/Tuesday/Wednesday/Thursday/Friday/
    Saturday/Sunday

Figure 7.24

Figure 7.23

11. The big saw in Figure 7.24 is so heavy and difficult to use that it takes two people to cut wood with it. What kind of logic gate might be used to represent this situation?

9. The two people in Figure 7.23 are about to start riding their tandem. What kind of logic gate could be used to represent this situation?
    (Hint – what is the input? What is the output?)

10. In most modern aircraft there is an alarm system which is turned on if the aircraft is not travelling fast enough and there is a danger it may stall. What kind of logic gate might be used to control this system?

CROSSWORD ON CHAPTER 7

Across

1 A _____ diagram simplifies the explanation of a circuit. (5)

8 Type of logic gate producing an output when either input is 1. (2)

9 The electromagnet inside the recording-head of a _____ is part of an analogue system. (4, 8)

10 Adding a NOT gate to an 8 across gate produces a _____ gate. (3)

11 A 1 is used to show the presence of an _____ or output. (5)

12 Digital logic is a two-state system, for example _____ and 13 across. (3)

13 See 12 across. (2)

14 A traditional _____ displays the time in analog form (5)

17 A digital _____ is non-continuous. (6)

18 A logic gate is _____ when it has a 1 output. (4)

19 A circuit _____ contains symbols that represent electronic components. (8)

21 A logic gate is _____ when it has a 0 output. (6)

22 In a _____ system, information is stored in binary code. (7)

Down

2 The _____ and stylus of a 4 down are transducers (9)

3 The information contained in a digital circuit is _____. (3, 10)

4 See 2 down. (6, 6)

5 The information contained in an analogue circuit is _____. (10)

6 A NOT gate added to an AND gate produces a _____ gate. (4)

7 Information fed *from* a circuit. (6)

15 Digital circuits handle two-state information such as _____ and low. (4)

16 Any _____ gate has a truth-table. (5)

20 Type of gate which gives an output when all inputs are 1. (3)

8 INTEGRATED CIRCUITS

8.1 WHAT IS AN INTEGRATED CIRCUIT?

Look at the computers shown in Figure 8.1.

Figure 8.1   A mainframe computer (top) and a modern 'micro'.

In just 40 years the size of a computer has shrunk from being large enough to fill an average sized living room to being small enough to hold in your hand. Also the modern computer:

a)   is much less expensive
b)   can perform more complicated tasks
c)   can handle more information.

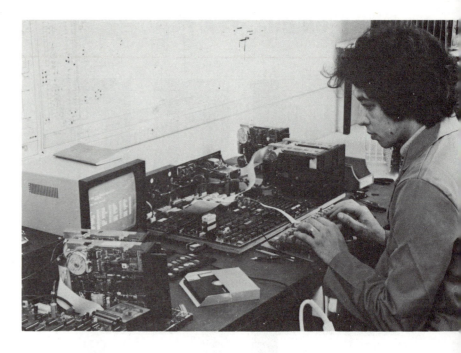

Figure 8.2   Testing integrated circuits.

These tremendous advances made in computer technology owe a lo to the development of components called *integrated circuits* or ICs

So far in this book all the circuits we have looked at have been buil using separate or 'discrete' components such as resistors, capacitors transistors, etc. But since the early 1960s it has become possible to construct single electronic components called integrated circuit to replace large numbers of discrete components.

Initially a single integrated circuit probably contained the equivalen of 50 or so discrete components. But today it is possible to manu facture integrated circuits that contain the equivalent of abou 1 000 000 components.

8.2 THE STRUCTURE OF AN INTEGRATED CIRCUIT

Most integrated circuits are built on a tiny piece of silicon called a *silicon chip*. Resistors, capacitors, diodes, transistors, etc., are formec in miniature on or near the surface of the chip, together with all the necessary connections. A simple explanation of how this may be done now follows.

MAKING AN INTEGRATED CIRCUIT

1. A single large crystal of silicon is grown from a bath of molten silicon. This crystal is then ground into the shape of a bar approximately 10 cm in diameter.

2. The bar is cut into wafers ¼ to ½ mm thick. The surfaces of these wafers are ground and polished to remove all marks and scratches.

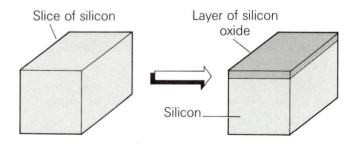

Cylinder of silicon   Wafers of silicon

Figure 8.3   A cylinder of silicon is sliced into wafers.

3. One surface of the wafer is coated with a thin layer of silicon oxide which is an excellent insulator.

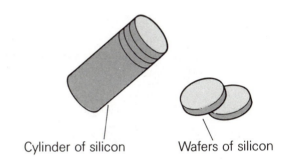

Slice of silicon   Layer of silicon oxide

Silicon

Figure 8.4   The wafer surface is coated with an insulator.

4. The silicon oxide is then coated with a thin layer of a special plastic which remains quite soft unless ultraviolet light is shone upon it.

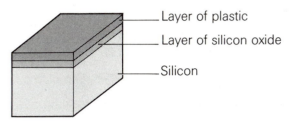

Layer of plastic
Layer of silicon oxide
Silicon

Figure 8.5   A thin layer of a special plastic is added.

5. A pattern for the circuit (more usually called a mask) is placed between the wafer and an ultraviolet light. Those areas that are exposed to the ultraviolet light harden, but those that are not exposed remain soft.

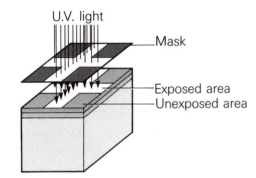

U.V. light
Mask
Exposed area
Unexposed area

Figure 8.6   The pattern for the circuit is marked out using ultraviolet light.

6. The wafer is treated with a chemical which removes the un-hardened plastic.

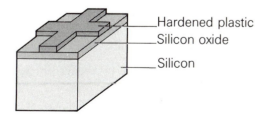

Hardened plastic
Silicon oxide
Silicon

Figure 8.7   Chemicals etch the pattern of the circuit.

7. The wafer is treated with a second chemical which removes any exposed areas of silicon oxide.

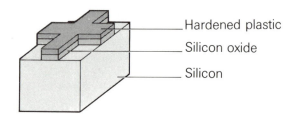

Hardened plastic
Silicon oxide
Silicon

Figure 8.8   The exposed areas of silicon oxide are removed.

8. The wafer is treated with a third chemical which removes the remaining hardened plastic.

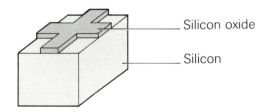

Silicon oxide

Silicon

Figure 8.9   The end result.

The end result is a network of silicon pathways and islands of silicon oxide.

9. Impurities are now added to the exposed silicon by heating the wafer to a high temperature while it is immersed in a vapour of boron or phosphorus. The addition of these impurities produces regions of n-type or p-type silicon.

10. The whole process from stage 4 onwards is repeated several times until all the layers have been completed. This results in the formation of diodes, resistors and transistors on the wafer (see Chapters 2 and 3).

11. Finally, a network of aluminium is deposited on the wafer. This connects together the diodes, resistors, transistors, etc., forming complete circuits.

To complete the manufacture of a wafer of integrated circuits may take several months. But because each wafer may have as many as 1000 integrated circuits formed on it and several wafers can be manufactured at a time, the cost of each integrated circuit is quite small.

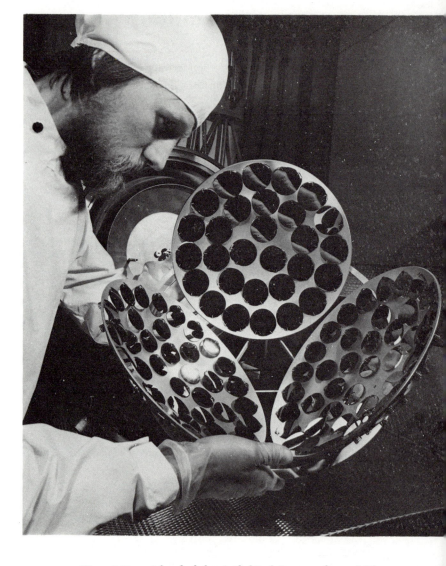

Figure 8.10   A hundred thousand chips being manufactured. They are prepared in dust-free rooms to ensure that they are perfect and dust-free.

After being cut up, the integrated circuits are packaged in such a way as to protect the chips and allow easy external connections.

There are two common types of packaging:

1. The *can* type
2. The *dual in line* (DIL) type

Figure 8.11 shows what they look like and how the terminals can be recognised.

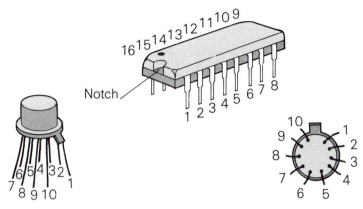

Figure 8.11   *Integrated circuit packaging. The 'dual in line' type (top). The 'can' type (left). The terminals can be recognized by the position of the tag on the can type (right, viewed from below) or the notch on the DIL type.*

8.3 BUILDING A CIRCUIT USING A CHIP

If we want to build a four-digit binary counter using resistors, capacitors, transistors, etc., we would need approximately 60 discrete components and probably three S-DeCs on which to mount the circuit. The circuit we are going to build in Experiment 8.1 is a four-digit binary counter which contains an integrated circuit. It needs just nine components and one S-DeC.

Figure 8.12   *A microboard, specially designed for use with integrated circuits.*

Experiment 8.1

To build a four-digit binary counter containing an integrated circuit

APPARATUS: S-DeC; connecting wire; wire strippers; 9 V battery; integrated circuit 4516B; 4 × LEDs; 4 × 820 Ω resistors (grey red brown); single pole knife switch

Integrated circuits – particularly the dual in line type are designed to be used not with S-DeCs but with 'microboards' (see Figure 8.12). To use IC 4516B on our circuit boards it is necessary to solder some connecting wire on to the pins. If the wires are soldered directly on to the pins of the IC, the heat from the soldering iron could damage the circuitry on the chip. To avoid this problem it is better to solder the wires on to a DIL socket before inserting the IC (see Figure 8.13).

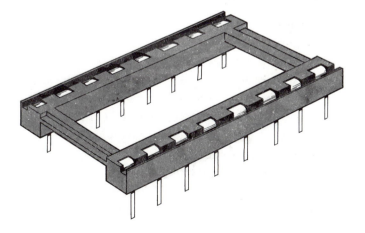

Figure 8.13   *A DIL socket.*

Soldering instructions

(Perhaps the soldering could be done by your teacher.)

a) Solder a piece of connecting wire 10 cm long to each of the following
    pins of the socket: 2, 6, 10, 11, 14, 15 and 16.

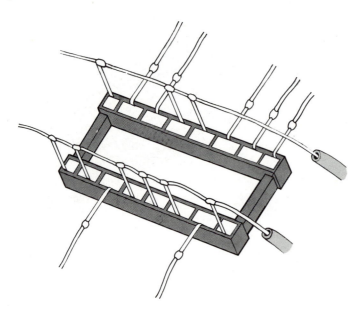

Figure 8.14   Stages of soldering.

b) Bend these pins outwards as shown in Figure 8.14.

c) Remove approximately 2 cm of the insulation from another piece of
    connecting wire approximately 10 cm long.

d) Place the bared wire so that it is in contact with pins 1, 3, 4, 5, 7 and 8.
    Solder the wire to each of these pins.

e) Remove approximately 2 cm of the insulation from another piece of
    connecting wire approximately 10 cm long.

f) Place the bared wire so that it is in contact with pins 9, 12 and 13.
    Solder the wire to each of these pins.

g) Place the IC pins into the socket, making certain that the IC pins
    correspond to the numbering of the socket pins (see Figure 8.14).

NOW

1. Set up the circuit as shown in Figure 8.15.

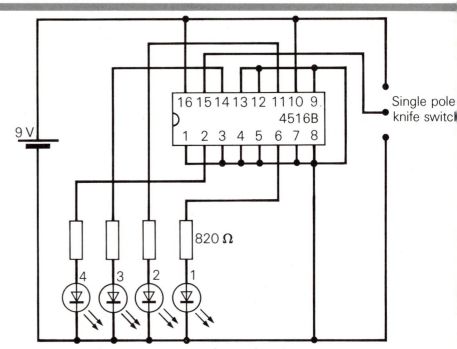

Figure 8.15(a)   Circuit diagram for Experiment 8.1.

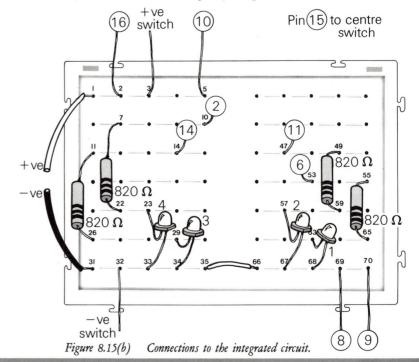

Figure 8.15(b)   Connections to the integrated circuit.

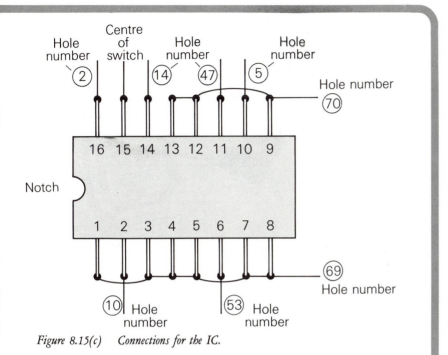

Figure 8.15(c)   *Connections for the IC.*

2. Move the switch from its central position over to the positive side then to the negative side and finally back to its central position. This complete movement feeds one pulse into the IC, which then alters the LED display, advancing it by one unit.

3. Set the display to 0000 by introducing pulses into the circuit until none of the LEDs is glowing. Now feed three pulses into the IC. Check the display with the binary table on page 66. Now feed in five more pulses. The LED display ought to show the binary code for 8 (3 + 5).

From Experiment 8.1 we can see that it is much easier and cheaper to build circuits which include integrated circuits than to build the equivalent circuit from discrete components.

.4 THE MICROPROCESSOR

Our brains continually receive small electrical signals from all parts of our bodies. These signals 'tell us' how we feel, e.g. hot, cold, tense, relaxed, etc. If our situation alters in any way, e.g. we feel pain, then our brains receive new messages which they 'process'. As a result of this processing, new signals are sent out and we react to the new conditions.

Figure 8.16   *New signals are sent out and we react to the new conditions.*

Some silicon chips work in a similar way to the above. They receive information from various sensors, such as thermistors, LDRs, etc., in the form of small electric currents. They process this information and then send out new electric signals to deal with the situation. Chips which are capable of doing this are called *microprocessors*.

The main uses of microprocessors are in 'control systems'. They work so efficiently in this application that it would be difficult to find an area of our lives which is not affected by them.

In washing machines for example, there is a chip which has been designed to receive electrical signals telling it which wash programme you have selected. When switched on, it locks the door, opens valves to allow water to flow in, warms up the water to the correct temperature and turns on and off the motor which rotates the drum.

Figure 8.17   *Programmable washing machine.*

In central heating systems, a chip receives electrical signals from various temperature sensors around the house. It processes these signals and then in accordance with the programme you have selected, it will turn the boiler on and off and direct the heat to where it is needed.

Figure 8.18   Central heating programmer.

The watch on the left of Figure 8.19 is a traditional mechanical timepiece. It is controlled by the movement of springs and cogs. The watch on the right is a modern one; it is controlled by a single microprocessor.

Both watches tell the time, but the microprocessor controlled watch

a)   is far more accurate
b)   is far more reliable because it contains fewer parts
c)   will tell us not only the time but also the day, date and month
d)   can be used as a very accurate stop watch
e)   will run for several years on one small battery.

As the above example shows, microprocessor controlled systems are generally better than mechanically controlled systems in many ways.

Figure 8.19   A traditional, mechanical timepiece compared with a digital watc

When the first traffic lights were introduced, they operated on 'fixe timings', for example each set of lights would be on green for tw minutes and then red for two minutes, regardless of whether it wa day or night or the roads were busy or quiet. Nowadays, the situatio is much improved by using microprocessor control. The 'processo receives signals 'telling it' the number of cars travelling on each road It then alters the timing of the traffic lights in order to improve th flow of traffic.

Figure 8.20   When the first traffic lights were introduced, they operated on fix timings.

In order to make a car more fuel efficient, the fuel system may be controlled by a microprocessor. This receives information about the outside temperature, the engine temperature, the engine speed, how hard the engine is being made to work, etc. It calculates the most efficient mixture of air and petrol for those conditions and then instructs the fuel injection system when it should introduce this into the cylinder. Without microprocessor control the fuel consumption would be considerably higher.

Figure 8.21   A car fuel system may now be controlled by a microprocessor.

Modern coin operated telephones contain a chip which records how much money has been put in, calculates the cost of the call, calculates if there is any change, displays this amount on a screen and finally delivers this when the caller has finished.

Figure 8.22   Modern coin operated telephones.

The chip also 'calls' the police if the telephone is being vandalised or robbed.

NO CASH? – NO PROBLEM!

At present if you want to buy something you need money and more often than not you need cash. This you could get from a dispenser similar to that shown in the illustration. At the heart of dispensers like these are one or more microprocessors. The dispenser recognises your own personal code, receives your request, dispenses the correct amount of money and alters your account to include the withdrawal. However, if modern technologists have their way, soon even the cash dispenser will be obsolete because we will not be using cash.

Figure 8.23   Cash dispenser.

If you go to the supermarket to buy some groceries, you may see that at the checkout, the cashier no longer reads the price tag stuck to each purchase. Instead he or she searches for the bar code – this is a pattern of thick and thin parallel lines which indicate what the item is and how much it costs. The code is passed over a small window next to the till. In doing so all the purchases are recorded and totalled, and an itemised bill is prepared for the customer's benefit. Also, a record of all purchases is kept by the supermarket so that it can quickly assess the stock and the sales of a particular item.

Figure 8.24   Example of a bar code.

Before leaving the supermarket, the bill must be paid. We may at present pay it with cash, but in the near future this may not be the case. Instead, a microprocessor will be connected to the computers in our banks. The cost of the purchases will be deducted from our account and an equivalent amount will be added to the supermarket's account. If this method of payment becomes widely accepted and used, there may eventually be no need for anyone to carry cash around with them at all.

? What would be the advantage of this system of payment?

? Would you need to carry something else instead of cash?

Figure 8.25   All these items contain integrated circuits.

Into the silicon slice below fit the following nine words.

CHIPS

PIN

CIRCUIT

WIRE

DOPED

IC

DIL

CAN

SILICON

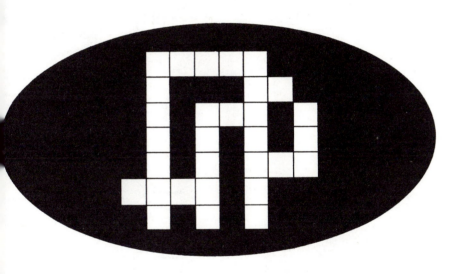

Write sentences including each of these nine words to show that you understand what each one means.

QUESTIONS ON CHAPTER 8

Write down the correct words to fill the gaps in these sentences.

1. A small piece of silicon crystal is called a _____ .

2. During the manufacture of an integrated circuit a crystalline bar of silicon is cut into _____ .

3. An integrated circuit which can absorb information, process it and then make decisions is called a _____ .

4. Integrated circuits are designed to be mounted not on S-DeCs but on _____ .

5. What are the three principal advantages of building circuits from integrated circuits rather than discrete components.

6. It is not a good idea to solder wires directly onto the connecting pins of an integrated circuit. Why?

7. How many pieces of equipment can you see in the diagram below which might contain integrated circuits?

APPENDIX A

ELECTRONIC COMPONENTS

WHAT IT IS	WHAT IT LOOKS LIKE	SYMBOL	WHAT IT DOES
9V battery			Pulls and pushes charges around a circuit.
Connecting wire			Provides a path through which current can flow.
Lamp/bulb (6V 0.06A)			Glows brightly if sufficient current flows through it.
Switch			Turns current in a circuit on or off.
Resistor			Reduces the current flowing in a circuit.
Variable resistor (rheostat)			By altering the value of a variable resistor the size of the current can be changed. The maximum resistance is usually marked on it.
Light dependent resistor (LDR)			When light shines on an LDR its resistance falls. In the dark its resistance is high.

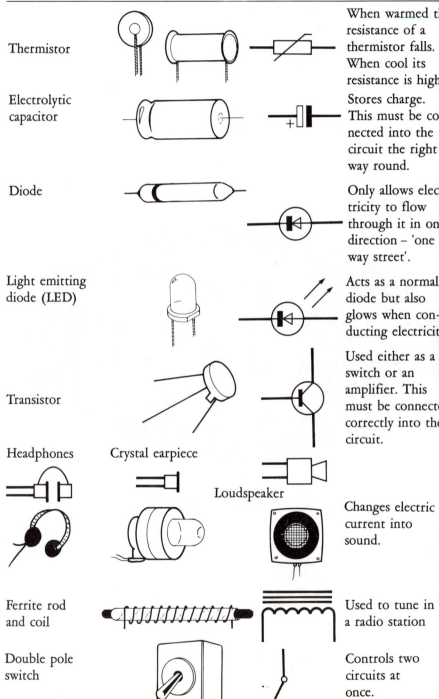

WHAT IT IS	WHAT IT LOOKS LIKE	SYMBOL	WHAT IT DOES
Thermistor			When warmed the resistance of a thermistor falls. When cool its resistance is high.
Electrolytic capacitor			Stores charge. This must be connected into the circuit the right way round.
Diode			Only allows electricity to flow through it in one direction – 'one way street'.
Light emitting diode (LED)			Acts as a normal diode but also glows when conducting electricity.
Transistor			Used either as a switch or an amplifier. This must be connected correctly into the circuit.
Headphones	Crystal earpiece	Loudspeaker	Changes electric current into sound.
Ferrite rod and coil			Used to tune in a radio station
Double pole switch			Controls two circuits at once.

APPENDIX B

LOOKING AFTER TRANSISTORS

Preparing transistors for the S-DeC

When the transistor 2N3053 is purchased, it has legs or terminals which are too short to be used on an S-DeC. It is necessary therefore to solder a short length of insulated connecting wire to each terminal. This must be done carefully. If the heat from the soldering iron causes the transistor to become hot it could be permanently damaged. The illustration below shows how the joint can be soldered without affecting the transistor.

By placing the pliers between the soldered joint and the transistor, any heat flowing up the terminals is absorbed by the jaws of the pliers.

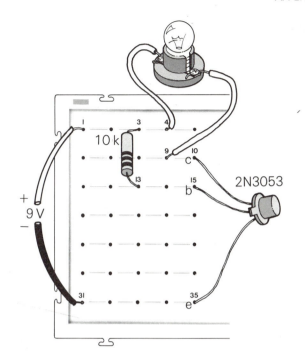

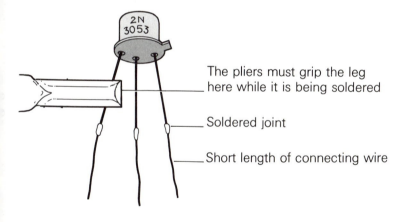

The pliers must grip the leg here while it is being soldered

Soldered joint

Short length of connecting wire

Testing transistors

If a transistor is incorrectly connected in a circuit it may be permanently damaged.

To check the condition of an npn transistor (e.g. 2N3053) build the circuit shown below. If the transistor is undamaged, the bulb will glow when the circuit is complete but will not glow if the 10 k resistor is removed.

If a transistor fails this simple test, it should be thrown away and replaced.

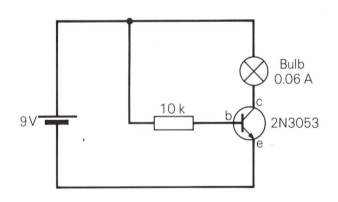

INDEX

SUPPLIERS

Electronic components supplies can be obtained from: R
Components Ltd, Tel. 01-360 0111.

For switches and headphones: Griffin and George, Tel. 01-997 3344

For S-DeCs: Roden Products, Tel. 03272 77461.